RD MARIAN WAY
LDC

ELECTRON
A SYSTEMS APP

ELECTRONICS
A SYSTEMS APPROACH

Alan Johnson

Barton Peveril College, Eastleigh

HODDER AND STOUGHTON

LONDON SYDNEY AUCKLAND TORONTO

ISBN 0 340 37156 0

First published 1987
Second Impression 1987
Third Impression 1988
Fourth Impression 1990
Fifth Impression 1991
Copyright © 1987 A Johnson

Typeset by Macmillan India Ltd., Bangalore 25, India.
Printed for Hodder and Stoughton Educational, a division of Hodder and Stoughton Ltd., Mill Road, Dunton Green, Sevenoaks, Kent by M & A Thomson Litho Limited, East Kilbride, Scotland.

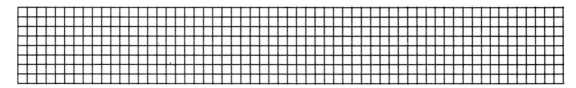

Contents

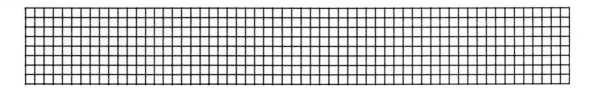

Acknowledgments

The author and publishers wish to thank the following for giving permission to reproduce photographs in this book: Arnold Photography, Austin Rover, BBC Enterprises, Marconi Communications Systems, RS Components, Bruce Roberts, Science Photo Library, Telecom Technology Showcase, Thames Systems Limited, Thorn EMI Instruments Limited. Units of the type used to illustrate this book are available from Electrolern, Lyburn Lodge, Nomansland, Salisbury, Wilts.

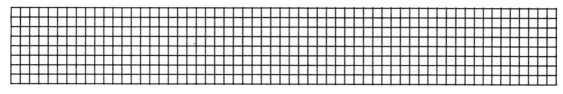

Preface

This book contains a course in electronics which is suitable for those studying the subject to GCSE level. It is also useful as an introduction to BTEC and GCLI courses and for the general reader interested in circuit design.

The study of electronics is usually approached either through the physics of semiconductors or through systems. This course adopts the systems approach. However, for those who feel that their understanding is improved by some knowledge of what is going on inside the components that they are using, a chapter on semiconductor devices (Chapter 3) is included. This chapter could well be omitted on a first reading.

The systems approach to electronics breaks complex electronic systems down into a number of subsystems joined together, and these subsystems into still more simple systems or components. In each case the emphasis is on what a system or component does rather than why it does it.

In the body of the book a number of subsystems or 'basic circuits' are developed which can be joined together to form a very large number of systems. Considerable use is made of variable resistors in the basic circuits so that trial-and-error methods can be substituted for calculation in adapting circuits to operate in particular situations. The basic circuits have been designed as far as possible so that they can be joined together without the loading problems that the beginner finds so intractable. The intention is to allow the reader to concentrate on designing complete systems that will satisfy a given specification and are likely to work.

The later chapters apply the systems method to some of the very complex systems concerned with computers and communication.

Some initial knowledge of electricity would be useful in the course but is not assumed, and the mathematical requirement is limited to simple arithmetic and some knowledge of graphs.

A. Johnson

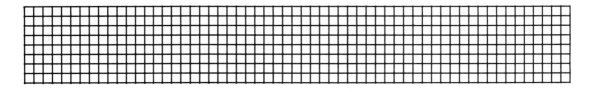

Introduction

Electronics gets its name from the *Electron*, a tiny particle which forms part of all materials. The subject has been described as 'the science and technology of controlling the flow of electrons to produce a useful result'.

It is the last part of this definition which is the most important. When an electronics engineer starts a new project his thoughts are not about the circuits he will use but about the job that the finished device will have to perform. He knows that his design will be judged on how well it performs its task and how cheaply it can be manufactured.

Electronic circuits can only deal with electrical quantities, and these are rare in the real world. Usually a device is required to convert the input (which may be a sound, a movement or a temperature) into an electrical *signal*, and another device is needed at the output to change the electrical signal into a form that the user would find useful. Devices of this kind are called *transducers*, and the general form of any *electronic system* is an electronic circuit sandwiched between an input transducer and an output transducer (see figure).

If an engineer was designing a burglar alarm, the input transducer would have to convert the movement or the sound made by the burglar into an electrical signal, and the output transducer would probably be a bell or a siren.

Once the transducers have been decided upon, the design of the electronics can begin.

If each new circuit involved starting at the beginning with a handful of individual components, the task of the designer would be difficult indeed. Luckily there is an easier way. Any complex electronic system can be broken

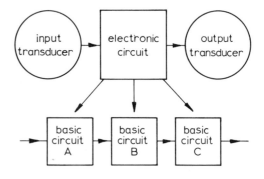

down into a number of simple subsystems connected together. Each subsystem will be able to perform a particular action on the signal between input and output, and a circuit will have been invented to perform this action. An experienced designer will remember a great many of these basic circuits, and so the circuit design will simply consist of selecting the correct basic circuits and joining them together. This method of design is called the *systems approach*. With this approach it is not necessary to know exactly what is going on inside an individual basic circuit or subsystem. All that is required is to know its function and something about its input and output so that it can be successfully joined to other circuits.

Some of the basic circuits are used so often that manufacturers have produced them as *integrated circuits*; that is, the whole circuit has been built on a tiny silicon slice and sold as a single component. The *microprocessor*, which is so often in the news, is just the most complicated and useful basic circuit that has yet been integrated. The microprocessor is special in that it is able to copy the functions of many other basic circuits and so replace them in systems.

Sometimes, of course, when the main system has been broken down into its subsystems there will be one that is new to the designer and he may be unable to find a circuit for it in the reference books. Then he will have to use his knowledge of the fundamentals of electronics to design a new basic circuit. This circuit will then be available for future projects.

The object of any book teaching electronics must be to turn the reader into a designer. The number of basic circuits available to the reader of this book will be limited, but sufficient for some useful design work to be attempted and for the working of many published circuits to be understood.

The process of learning electronics is in some ways the reverse of the design process. The first subsystems to be understood are the components themselves, but once again we are more interested in what they do than how they do it. The next stage is to combine these components to form some basic circuits. Lastly, we must learn the rules to be obeyed when joining the basic circuits together.

Fundamentals

1.1 The atom

All materials are made of atoms. All atoms contain the three main particles: *electrons*, *protons* and *neutrons*.

Protons and electrons have the electrical property called *charge*: protons in a form called *positive* charge, and electrons as *negative* charge. Charges of opposite sign are attracted to each other and charges of like sign repel each other.

The protons and neutrons cluster together at the centre of the atom, and round them circulate the electrons. The number of electrons and protons in an atom is usually the same and so, as all the charges are equal, the atom is neutral.

1.2 Metallic conductors

The atoms in a metal form a regular pattern called the *crystal lattice*. Some of the electrons are so loosely held by the attraction of their protons that they are free to move about inside the lattice. These *conduction* electrons move at great speeds

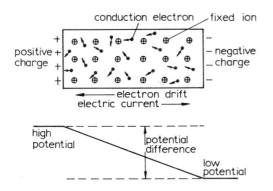

Figure 1.1 Conduction of electricity in metals

and their average energy is a measure of the temperature of the metal. If electrons leave their atoms then the atoms are an electron short and so have a positive charge. These positively charged atoms are called *ions*.

We can therefore imagine the inside of the metal as a fixed pattern of ions in three dimensions with the electrons moving about within it.

1.3 Current and potential difference

Figure 1.1 represents a piece of a metal with a positive charge at one end and a negative charge at the other. This is usually described by saying that the positive end is at a higher *potential* than the negative end, or that there is a *potential difference* (PD) between the ends. Whatever the description, the effect is the same: the electrons are attracted to the positive end and repelled by the negative, so that as well as their rapid movement within the lattice they drift towards positive.

The effect of this drift is to move negative charge from negative to positive. Provided that the potential difference is supplied by a device that can remove electrons from the positive end as they arrive and inject an equal number of electrons in at the negative end, the flow of charge will be continuous. The most common device of this type is the *voltaic cell* or *battery*. Energy is needed to maintain the electron flow, and so we can describe the potential difference between the ends of the metallic conductor as the energy needed to move one *coulomb* (unit symbol C) of charge from one end to the other. The potential difference will then be measured in *volts* (unit symbol V) and the energy in *joules* (unit symbol J).

$$\text{energy} = \text{charge} \times \text{PD}$$

$$E = QV$$

Potential difference is often called *voltage*.

If the voltage across the metal is constant then the same number of electrons will arrive at the positive end in each second. Each electron brings an equal charge, and so charge is arriving at a constant rate. The rate at which the charge arrives is called the *current*. This is measured in *ampere* (unit symbol **A**) and is represented by *I*, so that

$$Q = It$$

where *t* is the time in *seconds* (unit symbol s).

1.4 Resistance and resistors

The way in which the current in a conductor depends on the potential difference between its ends was investigated in 1826 by Georg Ohm, who described his results in his famous law:

For any metallic conductor, the current flowing is proportional to the potential difference between its ends.

This suggests that if we divide the potential difference (or voltage) by the current, the result will be a constant for any particular piece of metal. This constant is called the *resistance* of the metal and Ohm's law is most useful when expressed as an equation:

$$\text{resistance} = \frac{\text{voltage}}{\text{current}}; \qquad R = \frac{V}{I}$$

In electronics, metals usually occur in the form of wires. Compared with most other metals the resistance of *copper* is very low, and so copper wires covered with plastic are used to connect other components together. Plastics have no conduction electrons and therefore cannot conduct a current; they are good *insulators*.

Ohm's law is the most useful electrical law we have, but we must be careful how we use it. It should only be applied to metals, and then only if other factors that might alter the resistance of the metal do not change. The chief of these is *temperature*. The resistance of any metal increases slightly as its temperature rises, and passing a current through a wire is a way of raising its temperature. The fine wire inside a filament lamp is an example of this. The current in the filament raises its temperature to white

heat and its resistance to about double its value when cold.

Special alloys have been developed with resistances that vary little with temperature, and these are used in the manufacture of wirewound resistors. Any component which is used because of its resistance is called a *resistor*, and resistors form by far the most common component in electronic circuits.

The ideal resistor would be small and cheap to manufacture, its resistance would remain the same over long periods and for large variations in temperature, and it would be able to carry large currents without being destroyed by the heat produced. The ideal resistor does not exist.

Figure 1.2 shows some different types of resistors.

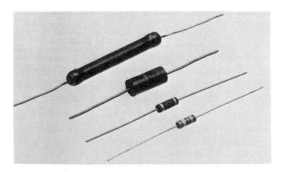

Figure 1.2 Different types of resistors. Wirewound; top: carbon moulded; centre; film; bottom

Wirewound resistors consist of a length of temperature-stable alloy wound on to a ceramic cylinder and insulated by a coat of enamel.

Advantages Good temperature stability, mechanical strength and heat resistance.
Disadvantages Large size, high cost and not available in very high values.

Film resistors have a thin film of metal, metal oxide or graphite deposited on the outside of the ceramic cylinder. A machine cuts a spiral groove round the cylinder, turning the film into a thin wire, until the resistor has the value required.

Advantages Nearly as good as wirewound, and smaller in size. They can be manufactured over the complete range of values that are required.
Disadvantages Not suitable for very-high-power applications.

Carbon resistors are moulded out of a mixture of a conductor such as graphite and an insulator.

Advantages Cheap to make.
Disadvantages Poor temperature stability, and easily destroyed by heat.

1.5 Preferred values

It is difficult to manufacture a resistor to an exact value, and so resistors are sold marked with a *tolerance* given as a percentage. A resistor with a tolerance of $\pm 10\%$ and sold as 100 ohms could be 10% greater or 10% less than 100 ohms or anything in between. It could therefore have any value between 90 ohms and 110 ohms, and there would be no point in manufacturing resistors with values within this range. The next resistor worth making is the one which, when reduced by 10%, has a value just larger than 110 ohms: that is, about 120 ohms. By the same argument the next value would be 150 ohms, the next 180 ohms and so on up to 820 ohms. The next value would be 1000 ohms, and the cycle would start again. These values are called *preferred values*, and a set will exist for each level of tolerance. Each cycle of the 10% tolerance set of preferred values contains 12 resistors, and it is called the E 12 series. There is an E 6 series for 20% resistors, and an E 24 series for 5% resistors.

1.6 The colour code for resistors

Resistors are small and it is difficult to write their preferred value on them in print that is large enough to read. A system of coloured bands has therefore been adopted in which each colour represents a number (Figure 1.3).

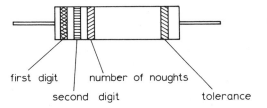

first digit   number of noughts
second digit   tolerance

Figure 1.3 Colour code for resistors

black	= 0	green	= 5
brown	= 1	blue	= 6
red	= 2	violet	= 7
orange	= 3	grey	= 8
yellow	= 4	white	= 9

The bands are nearer to one end of the resistor than the other, and it is with the band closest to the end that we start. This band gives the first digit in the value. The second band gives the next digit. The third band gives the number of noughts to be written after the two-digit number to give the value of the resistor in ohms.

Example *Band 1 of a resistor is red, band 2 is violet and band 3 is orange. What is the value of the resistor?*

The value is 27 000 ohms or 27×10^3 ohms. This would normally be given as 27 kilohms.

Resistors often have a fourth band which is gold or silver. Gold means that the tolerance of the resistor is $\pm 5\%$, silver means $\pm 10\%$ and no band at all $\pm 20\%$.

1.7 Circuit symbols and diagrams

Electrical circuits can be represented by diagrams using a number of conventional symbols. In some cases more than one symbol is in common use.

Component and comment	symbol
Connecting wire Assumed to have no resistance	
Resistor Used for its resistance	
Variable resistor Controls the current	
Potentiometer Controls the voltage	
Potentiometer as a variable resistor	
Voltaic cell Long stroke positive	
Battery Several cells in series	
Voltmeter Measures the PD between two points	
Ammeter Measures the current flowing through it	
Filament lamp Special type of resistor	

Figure 1.4 shows a circuit in which a 6 volt battery drives a current through a 2 ohm resistor. The current is measured by an ammeter. The ammeter reading could be calculated using $I = V/R$:

$$I = \frac{6}{2} = 3 \text{ amperes}$$

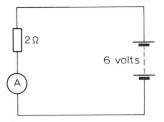

Figure 1.4

1.8   Potentiometers

A potentiometer consists of a resistance element, which may be of carbon composition or wire-wound, and a sliding contact which is able to

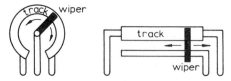

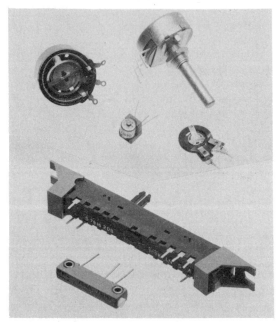

Figure 1.5   Various potentiometers

move along the element (Figure 1.5). In some the resistance element, called the *track*, is curved, and the *wiper* is attached to a rod which can be rotated by a knob. In others the track is straight and the wiper slides along it. In *preset potentiometers* the wiper is moved with a small screwdriver and is left in position when once set.

When the connection to the wiper and one end of the track is used, the potentiometer becomes a *variable resistor* or *rheostat*.

1.9   Resistors in series

A number of resistors R_1, R_2, and R_3 connected in series (Figure 1.6) could be replaced by a single resistor R_s of a value equal to the individual resistors added together

$$R_s = R_1 + R_2 + R_3$$

Figure 1.6   Resistors in series

1.10   Resistors in parallel

A number of resistors of value R_1, R_2 and R_3 connected in parallel (Figure 1.7) could be replaced by a single resistor R_p of the value given by the equation:

$$\frac{1}{R_p} = \frac{1}{R_1} + \frac{1}{R_2} + \frac{1}{R_3}$$

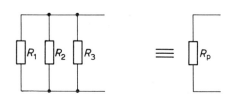

Figure 1.7   Resistors in parallel

Example *A circuit consists of a 6 volt battery, a 3 ohm resistor, an ammeter and a 4 ohm variable resistor connected in series (Figure 1.8). A voltmeter is connected across the 3 ohm resistor. What are the maximum and minimum readings of the ammeter and voltmeter?*

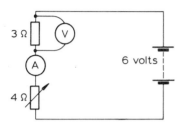

Figure 1.8

The maximum readings will be obtained when the variable resistor is turned down to zero. The total resistance in the circuit is now 3 ohm. From $I = V/R$,

$$I = \frac{6}{3} = 2 \text{ amperes}$$

Using $V = IR$,

$$V = 2 \times 3 = 6 \text{ volts}$$

This is not a surprising result as the voltmeter is connected to the battery by zero resistance paths.

The minimum readings will be obtained when the variable resistor is turned to its maximum of 4 ohms. The total resistance is $3 + 4 = 7$ ohms. From $I = V/R$,

$$I = \frac{6}{7} = 0.86 \text{ amperes}$$

This current flows through all the components in the circuit including the ammeter, which will therefore read 0.86 amperes

Applying $V = IR$ to the 3 ohm resistor,

$$V = 0.86 \times 3 = 2.58 \text{ volts}$$

The voltmeter therefore reads 2.58 volts. The other 3.42 volts is dropped across the variable resistor.

Example *Calculate the current in each of the resistors in Figure 1.9 and find the value of the PD across them.*

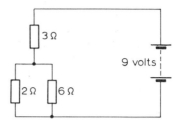

Figure 1.9

First the two resistors in parallel must be combined. From

$$\frac{1}{R_p} = \frac{1}{R_1} + \frac{1}{R_2} \quad \text{or} \quad R_p = \frac{R_1 R_2}{R_1 + R_2}$$

We obtain

$$R_p = \frac{2 \times 6}{2 + 6} = \frac{12}{8} = 1.5 \text{ ohms}$$

The total resistance is therefore $3 + 1.5 = 4.5$ ohms. From $I = V/R$,

$$I = \frac{9}{4.5} = 2 \text{ amperes}$$

This current will flow through the battery and the 3 ohm resistor, but it will split into two parts to pass through the 2 ohm and 6 ohm resistors. The PD across the 3 ohm resistor will be given by $V = IR$ as

$$V = 2 \times 3 = 6 \text{ volts}$$

leaving 3 volts across the resistors in parallel. For the 2 ohm resistor,

$$I = \frac{V}{R} = \frac{3}{2} = 1.5 \text{ amperes.}$$

For the 6 ohm resistor,

$$I = \frac{V}{R} = \frac{3}{6} = 0.5 \text{ amperes.}$$

1.11 Power in resistors

When a current passes through any resistor, electrical energy is converted into heat energy and the temperature of the resistor will rise. This heat is lost from the surface of the resistor into its surroundings. When the rate at which it loses heat is equal to the rate at which electrical energy is supplied, the temperature of the resistor will stay the same. The designer must make sure that this temperature is below the melting point of the resistor, and to help him each resistor is given a *power rating*. Power is the rate at which energy is supplied or used, and it is measured in *watts*.

We have seen (Sections 1.3, 1.4) that electrical energy is given by the equaion $E = QV$, and that $R = V/I$ and $Q = It$. Combining these,

$$E = IVt \qquad \text{or} \qquad E = I^2Rt$$

$$\text{or} \qquad E = \frac{V^2t}{R}$$

Equations for power (P) can be obtained from these equations by dividing by the time t. So

$$P = \frac{QV}{t} \qquad \text{or} \qquad P = IV \qquad \text{or}$$

$$P = I^2R \qquad \text{or} \qquad P = \frac{V^2}{R}$$

Example   *A 10 ohm resistor is rated at 3 watts. What is the greatest current that it can safely carry?*

Using $P = I^2R$,

$$3 = I^2 \times 10 \qquad \text{or} \qquad I^2 = 0.3$$

Therefore

$$I = \sqrt{0.3} = 0.55 \text{ amperes}$$

The maximum current is 0.55 amperes.

Potentiometers are also given power ratings. The maximum current that they will carry can be calculated in a similar way, but there is an added danger.

Example   *The speed of a motor of resistance 2 ohms is to be controlled by connecting it to a 10 volt battery and a 10 ohm, 100 watt potentiometer connected as a variable resistor (Figure 1.10). Is this a satisfactory arrangement?*

Using $P = I^2R$,

$$100 = I^2 \times 10 \qquad \text{or} \qquad I = 3.2 \text{ amperes.}$$

When the potentiometer is set to 10 ohms the total resistance is 12 ohms. Using $I = V/R$,

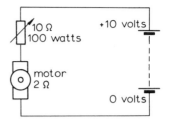

Figure 1.10

$$I = \frac{10}{12} = 0.8 \text{ amperes.}$$

This is less than 3.2 amperes, and so the potentiometer track is safe.

When the potentiometer is set to 5 Ω the total resistance is 7 Ω, and so

$$I = \frac{10}{7} = 1.4 \text{ amperes.}$$

The track is still safe.

When the potentiometer is set to 1 Ω the total resistance is 3 ohms, and so

$$I = \frac{10}{3} = 3.3 \text{ amperes.}$$

This is just over the maximum that the track can carry, and its temperature will rise.

If the resistance of the potentiometer is now turned down a little more, the current will rise still further and the track will burn out. Potentiometers usually burn out near one end of their track, and circuits must be designed so that their power rating cannot be exceeded even when they are reduced nearly to zero.

1.12   The capacitor

The *capacitor* is a device that stores electric charge. It cinsists of two plates of a conducting material separated by an insulator called the *dielectric*. A capacitor is usually named after its dielectric: thus a *paper capacitor* uses waxed paper, a *polyester capacitor* uses polyester sheet and a *mica capacitor* consists of thin sheets of silver-plated mica.

If a voltage is applied across a capacitor, charge flows on to it until there are enough extra electrons on the negative plate to produce a PD between the plates equal to the applied voltage. The charge needed to produce a voltage of one volt across the capacitor is called its *capacitance*, and depends on the size of the plates, the distance between them and the material used for the dielectric. The unit of capacitance is the *farad* and the symbol is *C*.

$$\text{charge} = \text{capacitance} \times \text{voltage}$$
$$Q = CV$$

1.13 Practical capacitors

An ideal capacitor would have a large capacitance in a very small size and yet be able to stand large voltages applied across it without the dielectric conducting. Figure 1.11 shows how a large plate area can be achieved in a small volume, and most capacitors use this construction. Alternate sheets of aluminium foil and dielectric material are rolled into a cylinder. Connecting leads are soldered to the aluminium, and the whole capacitor is covered by an insulator such as plastic.

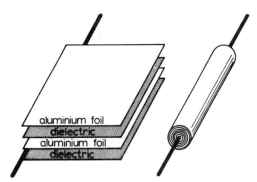

Figure 1.11 Construction of capacitors

Another way of obtaining a high capacitance in a small volume is to make the dielectric very thin. This unfortunately also reduces the maximum voltage that the capacitor can survive, and you will notice that high-voltage capacitors are larger than low-voltage capacitors of the same capacitance. If all capacitors were made by the method described above, those greater than one millionth of a farad (usually called one microfarad) would be too large. Above this value, *electrolytic capacitors* are used whenever possible.

In an electrolytic capacitor (Figure 1.12(a)) a conducting liquid or paste is used instead of a dielectric. This is called the *electrolyte*. When a voltage is first applied to the capacitor a current flows through the electrolyte, but soon an insulating layer builds up on the positive plate and the current stops. The insulating layer is the dielectric, and as it is only a few atoms thick the capacitance can be very high.

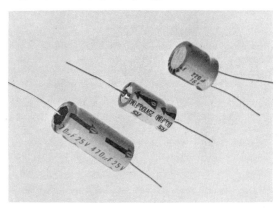

Figure 1.12(a) Electrolytic capacitors

The electrolytic capacitor has its disadvantages, however:

- It cannot be manufactured to exact values, and tolerances of up to ±80% are common.

- The voltage must always be applied in the same direction as when it was originally formed or the dielectric will be removed. One end is therefore marked in some way to show that it should be connected to positive. In Figure 1.12(a) the positive end is marked by a 'kink' in the case.

- It allows a small current, called *leakage* current, to flow through it.

- It changes its capacitance as it ages.

In spite of these disadvantages, electrolytics are so useful that many circuits would be impossible without them.

Another capacitor type which is sometimes required is the *variable capacitor* (Figure 1.12(b)). It is not just the area of the capacitor plates that decides what its capacitance will be, but the area of the two plates that overlap. Variable capacitors are designed so that this area of overlap can be varied as the control knob is turned. Some small variable capacitors or *trimmers* use a screw which varies the distance between two small plates. Many variables and trimmers have thin sheets of dielectric between the plates to increase their capacitance.

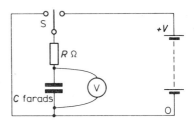

Figure 1.14

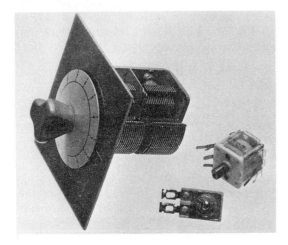

Figure 1.12(b)   Variable capacitors

In electrical circuit diagrams the capacitor is represented by the symbols given in Figure 1.13.

capacitor   electrolytic   variable
                      capacitor   capacitor

Figure 1.13   Symbols for capacitors

1.14   Charging and discharging a capacitor

Imagine that the conductor S is moved to the right in Figure 1.14. The capacitor is connected to the battery through the resistor. Charge will start to move on to the capacitor and, as moving charge is an electric current, a current flows through the resistor.

The current will be large at first, limited only by the resistor. As charge begins to build up on the capacitor, the voltage across it increases and less is left to drive the charging current through the resistor. The charging rate gets slower and slower as the voltage across the capacitor gets nearer to the battery voltage, and it will never quite reach it.

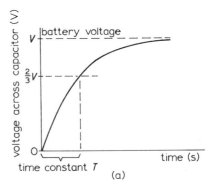

Figure 1.15 (a)

The voltage across the capacitor may never reach the battery voltage but it will certainly reach two-thirds of it, and the time it takes to do this is an important quantity called the *time constant* of the circuit (Figure 1.15(a)). The time constant is measured in seconds and is easily calculated from the following equation:

time constant = resistance × capacitance

$$T = RC$$

If the conductor S is now moved to the left the charge will flow out of the capacitor until, after a very long time, the capacitor is discharged (Figure 1.15(b)). In one time constant the voltage across the capacitor will fall by two-thirds of its original value.

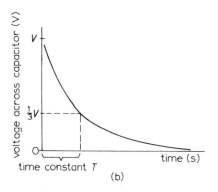

Figure 1.15 (b)

Example *A 100 microfarad capacitor and a 100 kilohm resistor are connected in series to a 12 volt supply. How long will it take for the voltage across the capacitor to reach 5 volts?*

To answer this question exactly would need a knowledge of mathematics beyond the scope of this book. Do we need to know the answer accurately? Remember that capacitors over 1 microfarad are usually electrolytics and that the tolerance on electrolytics is very large. If we calculated an exact answer it would not prove so exact in a practical situation. We shall try therefore to obtain an approximate answer in as simple a manner as possible, and to do this we must bend the truth a little.

Looking at Figure 1.15(a), you can see that the line up to a time equal to the time constant T is slightly curved. Let us pretend that it is exactly straight. The capacitor reaches two-thirds of its final value in one time constant. In this case the time constant T is given by

$$T = RC = 100\,000 \times \frac{100}{1\,000\,000}$$

$$= 10 \text{ seconds}$$

(Remember that, in using the formula, the resistance must be in ohms and the capacitance in farads.)

Two-thirds of the voltage is $2/3 \times 12 = 8$ volts. Thus the capacitor will reach 8 volts in 10 seconds or 1 volt in 10/8 seconds, and so 5 volts in

$$\frac{5 \times 10}{8} = 6.25 \text{ seconds.}$$

Example *To what value would the capacitor in the previous question have to be altered for the voltage across it to reach 3 volts in 7 seconds?*

The capacitor must reach 3 volts in 7 seconds or 1 volt in 7/3 seconds, and so 8 volts in

$$8 \times \frac{7}{3} = \frac{56}{3} = 18.7 \text{ seconds}$$

The time constant must be 18.7 seconds

$$C = \frac{18.7}{100\,000} = 187 \text{ microfarads.}$$

1.15 Capacitors and alternating voltage

The voltage supplied by a battery is constant and always has the same terminal as positive. It is called a *direct voltage*.

The voltage obtained from a mains socket is of a different kind. The voltage increases from zero to its *peak* positive value, then decreases to zero again. It then increases once again to the same value and back to zero, but this time the positive and negative terminals have reversed. This cycle is then repeated over and over again. Figure 1.16 shows a graph of voltage against time for two cycles of such an *alternating voltage*. The number of cycles completed per second is called the *frequency* and is measured in *hertz*. Other alternating voltages are of this shape but have different peak voltages and take different times for a cycle to be completed.

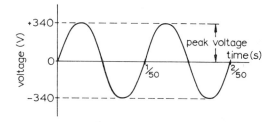

Figure 1.16   An alternating voltage

Now we must think about what would happen if an alternating voltage was connected to a capacitor (Figure 1.17). Remember that when the battery was first connected a current flowed, but this current became smaller and smaller as the capacitor charged until eventually it stopped. Thus we could say that after this charging period a capacitor did not conduct electricity.

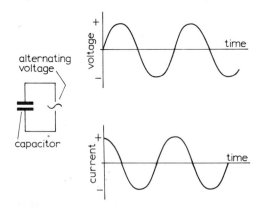

Figure 1.17   An alternating voltage connected to a capacitor

With an alternating voltage the capacitor is always gaining or losing charge as it attempts to make the voltage across it equal to the supply voltage. When the voltage is rising, current will be flowing on to the capacitor; when the voltage is falling, current will flow away from the capacitor. The charging current is an *alternating current*. Therefore if an alternating voltage is applied to a capacitor an alternating current flows just like it would through a resistor, although in fact no current actually passes through the capacitor.

If a capacitor connected to an alternating supply behaves like a resistor, there must be some quantity which could be compared with the resistance of a resistor. This quantity is called the *reactance* of the capacitor, and its value decreases as the capacitance or the frequency is made larger.

1.16   Capacitors and voltage pulses

If a voltage suddenly rises to a higher value, remains at this value for a short time and then returns to its original value, we would say that a *voltage pulse* had been generated.

Imagine a pulse like this applied to a capacitor. When the voltage suddenly rises, the voltage of *both* plates of the capacitor must rise with it because there will be no time for charge to flow on to the capacitor, and without it the two plates must be at the same potential. The effect is as if the capacitor was just a piece of connecting wire.

While the voltage remains at the higher value, charge will start to flow, but soon the pulse is over and the voltage returns to its original value.

It is therefore possible to connect two points by a capacitor so that they are insulated from each other but a voltage pulse can still be sent from one to the other.

1.17   Capacitors in series and parallel

If a number of capacitors are connected in parallel, it is just as though their plates had been joined to form two larger plates (Figure 1.18).

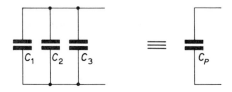

Figure 1.18   Capacitors in parallel

The total capacitance is therefore found by adding their individual capacitances together:

$$C_p = C_1 + C_2 + C_3$$

You will recognize this as similar to the equation for resistors in series, and so it will not surprise you to learn that the equation for capacitors in series (Figure 1.19) is like that for resistors in parallel:

$$\frac{1}{C_s} = \frac{1}{C_1} + \frac{1}{C_2} + \frac{1}{C_3}$$

Figure 1.19   Capacitors in series

It is sometimes useful to connect capacitors in parallel to make up a value which is not available, but capacitors are rarely connected in series.

1.18 The inductor

The *inductor* in its most simple form consists of a spiral coil of conducting wire. If a current is passed through the coil it takes on the properties of a bar magnet and is surrounded by a magnetic field. The total field is made up of small fields due to each of the turns in the coil, and the field of each turn cuts all the other turns. The strength of the fields can be greatly increased by sliding a bar of soft iron or similar material inside the coil. The inductor could then be used as an *electromagnet* to pick up pieces of iron.

However, its most interesting properties only appear when it is connected to a source of alternating voltage. The alternating voltage will produce an alternating current, which in turn gives rise to a magnetic field which varies continually in size and direction. When a magnetic field which is linked with a coil of wire changes its value or direction, a voltage is induced in the wire.

This is the result of the *laws of electromagnetic induction*. These laws also suggest that, in the case we are considering, the direction of the induced voltage will always oppose the alternating voltage which is indirectly producing it. The effect of the inductor and its induced voltage is therefore to oppose the applied voltage and so reduce the current.

With an alternating supply the inductor is another component which behaves rather like a resistor; as for the capacitor, this 'resistance' is called *reactance*.

The degree to which the turns of the inductor tangle with the magnetic field depends on the shape and number of turns on the coil, and is called its *inductance* (symbol L). The greater the inductance or the frequency, the greater the reactance. Inductance is measured in *henries* (unit symbol H).

1.19 Inductor, capacitor circuits

In many ways the inductor and capacitor have opposite properties, and a circuit combining the two is sure to be interesting.

We have seen that an alternating voltage or current is made up of a number of identical cycles, and that the number of these cycles that occur in a second is called the frequency. As the frequency increases, the reactance of an inductor increases and the reactance of a capacitor decreases. Thus for any pair of the components, a frequency must exist where the two reactances are equal. When this happens the circuit is said to be *tuned* to the frequency, and the combined reactance of the two components in parallel will be very large.

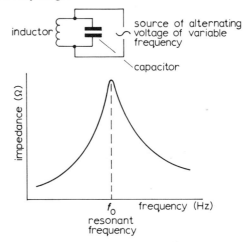

Figure 1.20 Variation of impedance with frequency

Figure 1.20 shows how this total reactance or *impedance* varies over a range of frequencies. At the special frequency called the *resonant frequency* the energy in the circuit is passed back and forward between the capacitor and inductor, being stored half the time in one and half the time in the other.

1.20 The transformer

A *transformer* consists of two coils of wire placed close enough together for the magnetic field of one to link with the other. Usually this linkage is increased by winding both coils on the same soft iron core.

If an alternating voltage is applied to one of the coils, called the *primary* coil, an alternating voltage is induced in the other or *secondary* coil. These primary and secondary voltages are connected by a simple equation:

$$\frac{\text{primary voltage}}{\text{secondary voltage}} = \frac{\text{number of turns on the primary}}{\text{number of turns on the secondary}}$$

Most electronic circuits require a voltage of between 5 and 12 volts, but the most convenient source of power, the mains, supplies 240 volts. A transformer with twenty times as many turns on its primary coil as it had on its secondary coil would give a secondary voltage of 240/20 volts if its primary coil was connected to the mains: that is, its secondary voltage would be 12 volts. We could call this a *step-down transformer* as it reduces the voltage, or a *mains transformer* because it is designed to operate from the mains (Figure 1.21).

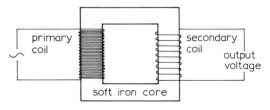

Figure 1.21   Step-down transformer

A transformer by itself will not power our circuits, however, because its output voltage is alternating. A device called a *rectifier* is required which can convert the alternating voltage to a direct voltage, and for this we must wait until Chapter 4.

Summary

Electrical quantities and symbols

Quantity	Symbol	Unit	Unit symbol
Charge	Q	coulomb	C
Current	I	ampere	A
Voltage or PD	V	volt	V
Energy	E	joule	J
Power	P	watt	W
Resistance	R	ohm	Ω
Time	t	second	s
Capacitance	C	farad	F
Inductance	L	henry	H
Frequency	f	hertz	Hz

The units in this table are often found to be too big or too small to conveniently represent the quantities in electronics, and certain prefixes (or prefix symbols) are placed in front of the basic units (or unit symbols) to give a number of larger and smaller units (or unit symbols).

Metric prefixes

Prefix	Prefix symbol	Multiplying power		
mega	M	1 000 000	or	10^6
kilo	k	1000	or	10^3
milli	m	0.001	or	10^{-3}
micro	μ	0.000 001	or	10^{-6}
nano	n	0.000 000 001	or	10^{-9}
pico	p	0.000 000 000 001	or	10^{-12}

Examples:

470 000 V = 470 kV   0.000 003 3 F = 3.3 μF

6800 kΩ = 6.8 MΩ 0.0082 μF = 8.2 nF

Printed resistor code

This is a British Standard code (BS 1852) which enables any resistor value to be written down using only three or four symbols. It avoids the use of the decimal point, which is easily lost in diagrams. A few examples will make the system clear.

0.1 Ω	= 0R1	0.22 Ω	= 0R22
100 Ω	= 100R	1.5 kΩ	= 1K5
560 kΩ	= 560K	3.3 MΩ	= 3M3
2.7 kΩ	= 2K7		
27 kΩ	= 27K		
1 MΩ	= 1M0		

We will use the SI units (eg 0.1 Ω) throughout diagrams in this book although in other places you may see the British Standard Code used. A letter indicating tolerance may be added after the value.

M = $\pm 20\%$ K = $\pm 10\%$ J = $\pm 5\%$

G = $\pm 2\%$ F = $\pm 1\%$

Equations

$$Q = It \qquad E = QV \qquad P = \frac{QV}{t}$$

$$Q = CV \qquad E = IVt \qquad P = IV$$

$$E = I^2Rt \qquad P = I^2R$$

$$E = \frac{V^2t}{R} \qquad P = \frac{V^2}{R}$$

Series:

$$R_s = R_1 + R_2 + R_3 \qquad \frac{1}{C_s} = \frac{1}{C_1} + \frac{1}{C_2} + \frac{1}{C_3}$$

Parallel:

$$\frac{1}{R_p} = \frac{1}{R_1} + \frac{1}{R_2} + \frac{1}{R_3} \qquad C_p = C_1 + C_2 + C_3$$

$$\text{capacitor reactance} = \frac{1}{2\pi f C}$$

$$\text{inductor reactance} = 2\pi f L$$

All of these equations are useful, but one is essential and must be remembered in all its forms:

$$R = \frac{V}{I} \qquad I = \frac{V}{R} \qquad V = IR$$

When using these three equations a consistent set of units must be chosen. Possible sets are:
volts (V), amperes (A) and ohms (Ω);
volts (V), milliamps (mA) and kilohms (kΩ);
volts (V), microamps (μA) and megohms (MΩ).

Questions

1 Calculate the values needed to fill in the blank spaces in the table below. Give your answer in the most suitable unit.

Current	Potential difference	Resistance
3 A	12 V	—
2 A	—	7 Ω
—	9 V	40 Ω
8 mA	—	5 kΩ
2 mA	4 kV	—
—	6 V	66 MΩ
150 μA	—	30 kΩ
—	50 mV	300 Ω

2 A PD of 12 V is applied to a 15 Ω resistor. Calculate

(a) the current in the resistor

(b) the quantity of *charge* passed in 5 min

(c) the energy converted to heat in 100 s

3 Find the combined resistance of a 33 kΩ resistor and a 47 kΩ resistor when connected (a) in series (b) in parallel.
A 10 V supply is connected across the resistors in both (a) and (b). What is the current flowing in the 33 kΩ resistor in each case?

4 What are the values of the following resistors in (a) ohms and (b) kilohms?

	Band 1	Band 2	Band 3	Band 4
(1)	brown	black	orange	silver
(2)	green	blue	brown	gold
(3)	grey	red	yellow	—
(4)	yellow	violet	orange	gold
(5)	orange	white	black	silver

What other information can you deduce about the resistors?
Write down the values of these resistors using BS 1852.

5 The voltage across the 150 Ω resistor in the circuit shown was found to be 3 V. Calculate the current in the resistor and the supply voltage *V*.

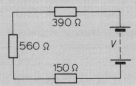

6 What is the maximum current that a 1.5 kΩ, 5 W resistor can safely carry?

What would happen if this current was exceeded?
What would be the maximum voltage that could safely be connected across this resistor?

7 Calculate the charge stored in a capacitor of 50 F if a PD of 20 V is applied across it. The PD is now removed and the charged capacitor connected in parallel with another uncharged 50 F capacitor. What will be the charge stored by each capacitor, and what will be the voltage between their plates?

8 What is the time constant for a 100 μF capacitor and a 4.7 kΩ resistor? If a PD of 9 V is applied across the resistor and capacitor, how long will it take for the voltage across the capacitor to reach (a) 6 V (b) 2 V?

9 A *mains* transformer with 800 turns on its primary coil is required to step down the 240 volt AC supply to 6 V. How many turns should be wound on its secondary coil?

2

Electrical measurement

2.1 The moving-coil ammeter

An ammeter is a device for the measurement of electric current, and the most common form consists of a coil of wire mounted so that it is able to turn between the poles of a magnet (Figure 2.1). According to a law discovered by Faraday, a force acts on any conductor carrying a current when it is in a magnetic field. In this case the force will make the coil rotate. Coil springs are fitted to the top and bottom of the coil and perform two functions. They allow the current to enter and leave the coil, and they provide a force in the opposite direction which controls the angle through which the coil turns. We now have a system in which the angle turned by the coil is proportional to the current passed through it. A pointer and scale are added, and the result is a moving-coil ammeter.

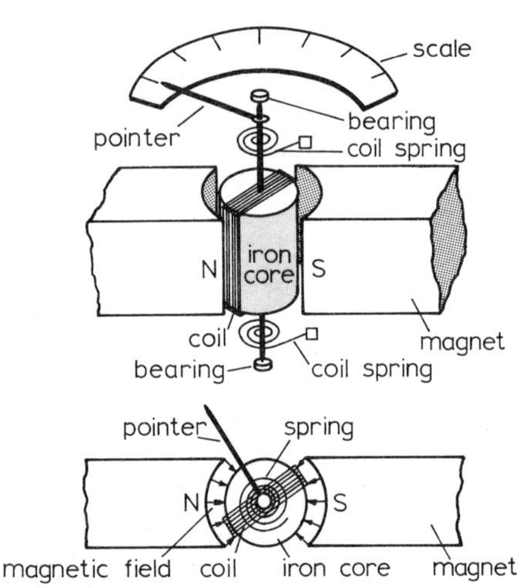

Figure 2.1 Moving-coil ammeter

The wire used on the coil is very fine and can carry only a very small current, and so the instrument is designed to give a *full-scale deflection* (FSD) for a current of only a few milliamperes or even microamperes. Ammeters which can measure currents of up to about 100 μA are called *microammeters* and those with an FSD up to 100 mA are called *milliammeters*. Sometimes we need to convert a microammeter into a milliammeter, or either of these into an ordinary ammeter capable of measuring large currents. To do this a low resistance called a *shunt* is connected in parallel with the basic meter. The value of the shunt is chosen so that most of the large current goes through it, and only enough to produce a suitable deflection goes through the meter.

Example *Convert a milliammeter of FSD* 20 *mA and resistance* 100 Ω *into an ammeter capable of measuring currents up to* 5 *A*.

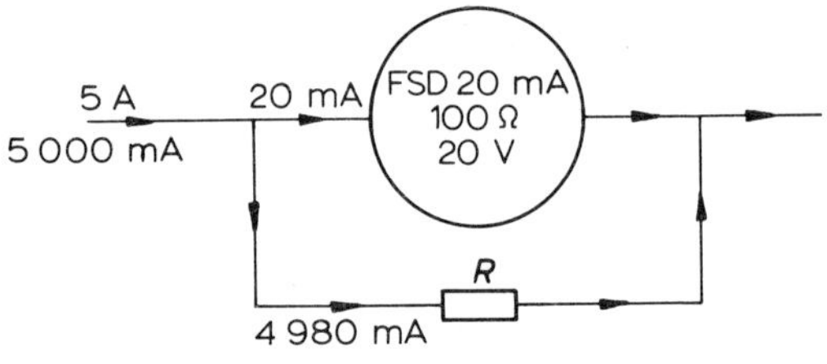

Figure 2.2

We have to connect a shunt in parallel with the milliammeter. This shunt will have a value *R* such that, when 5 A flows into the combination, only 20 mA will flow through the meter and the other 4980 mA will flow through the shunt (Figure 2.2).

The voltage across the meter and the shunt is

the same, as they are in parallel. The voltage across the meter is given by $V = IR$:

$$V = 20 \times 0.1 = 2 \text{ V} \qquad (100 \, \Omega = 0.1 \text{ k}\Omega)$$

Using $R = V/I$ for the shunt,

$$R = \frac{2}{4980} = 0.0004 \text{ k}\Omega = 0.4 \, \Omega$$

The resistance of the shunt would be $0.4 \, \Omega$

You will see from the example that the shunt is likely to have a low resistance. If an ammeter is to be perfect it must not alter the current that it is measuring.

An ideal ammeter should have no resistance.

To measure the current in a circuit, the circuit must be broken and the ammeter inserted in the gap. Always use an ammeter with an FSD larger than the expected current.

2.2   The moving-coil voltmeter

The moving-coil voltmeter is simply an ammeter with a series resistor. A particular voltage is able to drive a current through this resistor according to Ohm's law, and the ammeter measures this current.

Example   *Convert a milliammeter of FSD 20 mA and resistance 100 Ω into a voltmeter capable of measuring voltages up to 5 V (Figure 2.3).*

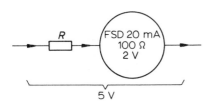

Figure 2.3

If a voltage of 5 V is going to drive a current of 20 mA, then the total resistance will be $5/20 = 0.25$ kΩ or 250 Ω.

The meter has a resistance of 100 Ω, and so the series resistor must be $250 - 100 = 150 \, \Omega$.

An ideal voltmeter should have infinite resistance.

It is impossible to make a moving-coil voltmeter of infinite resistance, but it is important that its resistance is as high as possible. The resistance of a voltmeter depends on the current required to produce FSD and the voltage it has to measure. The resistance is given as *ohms per volt*. If a particular voltmeter has 100 Ω/V, then its resistance is 100 Ω if its FSD is for 1 V; 1000 Ω if its FSD is for 10 V; and 2 kΩ if it reads up to 20 V. You just multiply the Ω/V by the voltage range.

The meter in the example would be 50 Ω/V. A voltmeter based on a milliammeter of FSD 1 mA would give a resistance of 1000 Ω/V. The best moving-coil voltmeters use a 50 μA meter, giving resistances of 20 kΩ/V.

2.3   The ohmmeter

The ohmmeter is not really a meter but a circuit which includes an ammeter rescaled to read in ohms. The circuit is shown in Figure 2.4. In this ohmmeter the ammeter used has FSD for 1 mA.

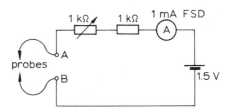

Figure 2.4   Circuit for ohmmeter

When the probes A and B are short-circuited together the current is determined by the total resistance in the circuit. Using a 1.5 V dry cell, this resistance will be $1.5/1 = 1.5$ kΩ. This is made up by adding the resistance of the meter, the fixed 1 kΩ resistor and part of the potentiometer. A potentiometer is used because a new dry cell has a voltage rather more than 1.5 V, and this voltage falls during the life of the cell. Each time the ohmmeter is used its leads are shorted and the potentiometer adjusted to give FSD.

Suppose now that a number of known resistors were connected between A and B. Each value would give a current reading less than FSD. Figure 2.5 shows the meter reading plotted against the resistance. If an unknown resistor was now connected between A and B and the meter reading was noted, the value of the resistor could be found from the graph. A more convenient method is to mark the resistance values directly on to the meter scale. The graph is a curve and so the ohm scale will not be linear: that is, the gaps between equal numbers of ohms will not be the same, but instead the values will crowd together as they become larger.

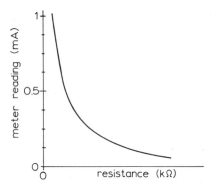

Figure 2.5   Meter reading against resistance

All ohmmeters read resistance from 0 to infinity, and so it is useless to talk about their FSD. Instead we quote the resistance value that gives a mid-scale reading. This resistance is equal to the internal resistance of the ohmmeter. In the circuit of Figure 2.4 this is 1.5 kΩ.

2.4   The analogue multimeter

A good moving-coil microammeter is expensive and it is sensible to get the most use out of it. A multimeter uses a single meter plus a number of shunts and series resistors to convert it into ammeters and voltmeters of various values of FSD (Figure 2.6). The different shunts and resistors are selected by plugging the leads into different sockets or by elaborate switches. Multimeters also contain a battery so that an ohmmeter circuit can be included, and usually a diode bridge (Section 3.5 and Figure 4.3) is connected to the meter so that alternating voltages and currents can be measured.

With so many ranges the scales of a multimeter can become very crowded and care is needed when reading them. For example, there may be ranges reading up to 2.5, 25 and 250 volts but only one scale numbered up to 25. You have to put the decimal point in the correct place. Many multimeter scales are backed by a mirror. You will only get the correct reading if you look

straight at the scale, and you will know that you are doing this when the pointers image is invisible behind the pointer.

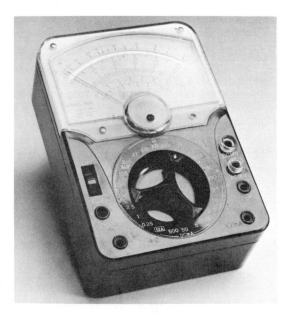

Figure 2.6   Analogue multimeter

2.5   The digital voltmeter

The digital voltmeter does not give a continuous reading of the input voltage like an analogue (moving-coil) voltmeter. Instead the voltage applied to its input is sampled at regular intervals, often 1 second, and its value displayed as a number by some form of numerical display. The meter shows the old value until it receives the new one, and so the input voltage could change its value and then change back again between samples without the voltmeter or its operator knowing.

In theory an analogue meter can be read as accurately as we like. In practice, reading accuracy is limited by the width of the pointer and the number of scale markings.

Once a voltage is displayed as a number we automatically limit its accuracy. Suppose a digital voltmeter had a two-digit display and was measuring a voltage of 27.3 volts. The meter can only display this as 27 or 28. The analogue meter would give a deflection between 27 and 28 and we could estimate the fraction 0.3. In this example the analogue meter appears to be more accurate than the digital. The strength of the digital display is that more digits can always be added to make it as accurate as we like, but it is difficult to increase the accuracy with which we can read a pointer. A digital meter with four digits is more accurate than any analogue meter.

The other advantage of the digital meter is its high resistance, often as high as 10 megohms. It therefore much more nearly approaches an ideal voltmeter.

It is not necessary to know how an instrument works to be able to use it, but a brief description of the working of a digital voltmeter will be given as an example of a system. Figure 2.7 shows one as a block diagram. If you return to this system after you have read the rest of the book, many of the subsystems will be familiar to you.

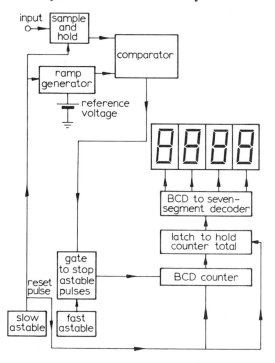

Figure 2.7 Block diagram of digital voltmeter

In Figure 2.7, the slow astable produces a pulse at intervals. This resets the output of the ramp generator to zero, and enables the sample and hold so that it does exactly as its name implies – samples the input and holds it until the next slow clock pulse. The slow astable pulse also resets the binary-coded decimal (BCD) counter to zero having transferred its contents to a latch.

When the reset pulse is over the output of the ramp generator starts to increase linearly. The comparator compares the ramp voltage with the sampled input and when they are equal (or the ramp is just the larger), the output of the comparator changes, which stops the fast clock pulses entering the BCD counter. During the time the ramp is increasing the counter has been counting fast astable pulses and now contains the total. At the next slow pulse this total is transferred to the latch, decoded and displayed on the seven-segment display. The fast astable has a frequency which makes the number displayed numerically equal to the input voltage.

To maintain accuracy the ramp generator must always ramp up at the same rate and the fast astable must have a constant frequency. To achieve this the input to the ramp generator is from a standard cell or other source of constant voltage, and the frequency of the astable is controlled by the oscillations of a quartz crystal.

2.6 The digital multimeter

The digital multimeter (Figure 2.8) provides the same functions as the analogue multimeter but it is based on a digital voltmeter rather than a moving-coil ammeter. Unlike the analogue meter it has the same input resistance, usually 10 MΩ, on all its voltage ranges. The basic voltmeter measures the lowest voltage and the higher ranges use potential dividers to reduce the voltages to this value. (For the working of a potential divider see Section 4.6.) Currents are measured by passing them through a known resistor and measuring the voltage across it. To measure resistance a circuit inside the meter drives a constant current through it and the meter measures the voltage produced.

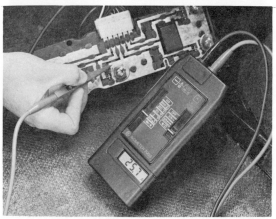

Figure 2.8 Digital multimeter

2.7 Analogue multimeter versus digital multimeter

The digital meter is usually more accurate, and with its high input resistance is less likely to alter what it measures. The analogue meter does not require a power supply, and when the voltage being measured is changing it is the only choice.

2.8 The cathode ray oscilloscope

The cathode ray oscilloscope (CRO) is a most useful tool and any serious student of electronics must learn to use it well. Figure 2.9 shows the front panel of a simple oscilloscope. The following notes are based on this instrument but can easily be adapted for others.

Figure 2.9 Front panel of a simple oscilloscope

Imagine that the CRO has just been plugged into the mains supply and switched on. The indicator light next to the right of the screen will light up, and after a short time a line or dot may appear on the screen. If there is no sign of the trace (as the line or dot is called) turn the

brightness control to a midway position, and if the trace is still absent press the locate button. This will make a fuzzy trace appear on the nearest part of the screen. If this trace is near the bottom release the locate button and move the Y-shift control upward; if the trace is at the top of the screen the Y-shift can be used to move it down. In the same way, X-shift can be used to move the trace on to the screen if it is near either side.

Once the trace has been found, make the following adjustments:

- Turn the AC/DC switch to DC.
- Turn the trigger control to off (clockwise in this CRO).
- Turn the time base control to 0.1 ms.
- Turn the volts/cm control to 1 volt.
- Use the X-shift and Y-shift controls to position the line across the centre of the screen.
- Adjust the brightness to the lowest acceptable brightness of the trace. It will help if the screen is shielded from direct light.
- Use the focus control to obtain as sharp a line as possible.

2.9 The CRO as a DC voltmeter

Connect the DC voltage to be measured to the Y-input sockets, connecting the earth socket first. Note which way the trace moves: upward shows that the earth input is negative. If the trace moves only a small distance, increase the gain by turning the volts/cm control to a lower value. If the trace goes off the screen, turn the same control in the opposite direction. Suppose the trace moves 3.5 squares up the screen when the volts/cm control is set to 5. The input voltage is $3.5 \times 5 = 17.5$ volts and is positive.

2.10 The CRO as an AC voltmeter

Connect the AC voltage to the input terminals. The AC/DC switch should still be on DC. You will see a rather confusing blur moving across the screen. If you note the height of this trace and use the setting of the volts/cm control to convert it to a voltage; you will have the *peak-to-peak* voltage of the input signal.

It is better, however, to see what you are measuring, and to do this turn the trigger control.

At some point the trace will become a single line which is a graph of voltage against time for the input signal. The peak-to-peak voltage is now obtained by measuring in screen squares the distance vertically between the highest and lowest part of the trace and then multiplying the result by the setting of the volts/cm control.

The *peak* voltage is half the peak-to-peak value. If the graph is that of a *sine wave* the *root-mean-square* (RMS) voltage can be found by dividing the peak value by $\sqrt{2}$ or 1.414.

Assuming that the volts/cm control (also called the *Y*-amplifier control) is set to 2 volts/cm, the trace of Figure 2.10 is a sine wave of peak-to-peak voltage 8 V, peak voltage 4 V and RMS voltage 2.82 V.

2.11 The measurement of period and frequency using the CRO

Use the procedure described in the previous sections to obtain a steady trace on the screen. Choose a setting of the time base control that gives at least one and not more than three complete waves on the screen. Make sure that the wave is as far above the centre line as it is below it. Starting at the point where the trace crosses the centre line in the upward direction, measure the number of squares and part squares until the trace cuts the centre line again in an upward direction at the start of the next wave. Multiply the reading by the setting of the time base to obtain the *period* of the wave, i.e. the time taken for one wave.

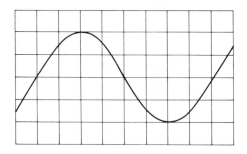

Figure 2.10 Sine wave

In Figure 2.10 the length of one wave is 8 squares. If the time base was set to 0.1 ms, the period is 0.8 ms. The frequency of the wave is 1/period, and so the frequency of the wave in

Figure 2.10 is $1000/0.8 = 1250$ Hz or 1.25 kHz. The 1000 occurs because there are 1000 ms in one second. If the time base setting was in microseconds then we would use 1 000 000 instead of 1000.

2.12 The AC/DC switch

It is quite common for a signal to consist of a mixture of AC and DC. Figure 2.11 shows the graph of such a signal plotted against time. Usually it is the AC part which interests us, but if we try to increase the amplitude of this part by turning up the *Y*-amplifier gain on the CRO we amplify the DC as well and the trace disappears off the top of the screen.

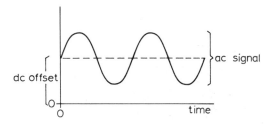

Figure 2.11 Signal consisting of mixture of alternating and direct currents

A capacitor will let AC through it but block DC (Section 1.15). If a capacitor is connected in series with the *Y* input of the CRO, the DC part of the signal will be removed and we can examine the AC. The AC/DC switch switches this capacitor in and out of the circuit.

2.13 Cathode rays and their production

A cathode ray is the name given to a high-speed beam of electrons. The electrons are usually produced by a process called *thermionic emission*. When metals (or better still, certain metal oxides) are heated, electrons 'boil off' from the surface. These electrons can be accelerated to high speeds by attracting them to a positively charged electrode called an *anode*. This anode is made cylindrical so that the electrons can pass through it and continue on as a beam of cathode rays. The heated metal (called the *cathode*) and the anode must be in an evacuated container or the electrons will collide with the air molecules.

2.14   The cathode ray tube

The cathode ray tube (CRT) is the heart of a CRO. It consists of a strong glass tube with an *electron gun* (cathode and anode) at one end and a *screen* at the other (Figure 2.12). Electrons are emitted by the cathode, are accelerated by the anode and finally hit the screen at a speed of nearly one-tenth the speed of light. The screen is covered with a material called a *phosphor* which emits light when an electron strikes it, and so a spot of light is formed at the centre of the screen.

The anode is in two parts at different positive voltages, and the voltage of one can be varied by a potentiometer. This potentiometer is mounted on the front panel and forms the *focus* control. Another potentiometer on the front panel supplies a negative voltage to an electrode called the *grid* situated between the cathode and anodes. This electrode repels electrons and therefore limits the number reaching the screen, so forming a *brightness* control. Between the anodes and the screen are two further pairs of electrodes. Positive and negative voltages applied to the *Y-plates* moves the spot up and down the screen, and voltages on the *X-plates* moves the spot in a horizontal direction.

2.15   The CRO as an electronic system

Figure 2.13 shows a block diagram of the subsystems connected to the CRT. The signal to be examined is applied between the *Y-input* and earth. Passing the *AC/DC switch* and capacitor as described in Section 2.12, the signal enters the *Y-amplifier*. This amplifier is able to amplify AC or DC, and has a number of fixed voltage gains selected by a switch on the front panel called *Y-amplifier gain* or *volts/cm*. The output from the Y-amplifier goes to the *Y*-plates of the CRT and to a trigger circuit.

The signal will now move the spot up and down the screen an amount depending on the strength of the signal and the setting of the volts/cm control. To produce a graph of the signal against time the spot will have to be moved horizontally across the screen at the same time. This is the function of the *time base*. This circuit generates a voltage ramp which moves the spot across the screen and then rapidly returns the voltage to its original value. This part of the time base waveform is called the *flyback* and it returns the spot to the left-hand side of the screen ready to start again. If the input wave repeats itself at

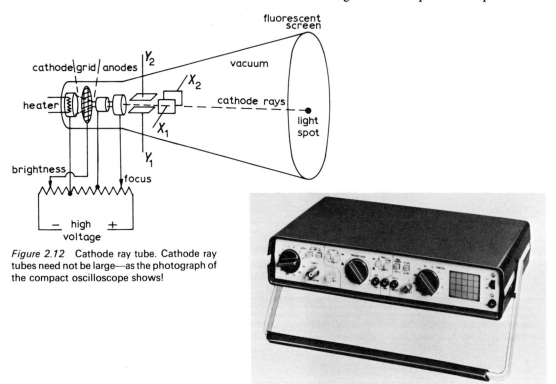

Figure 2.12   Cathode ray tube. Cathode ray tubes need not be large—as the photograph of the compact oscilloscope shows!

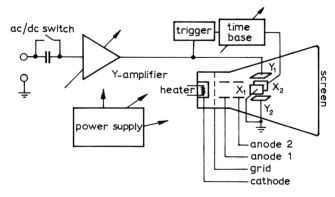

Figure 2.13 Block diagram of subsystems connected to cathode ray tube

regular intervals and the time base operates at the same frequency, a number of graphs will be drawn on the screen one on top of the other so that a stationary picture is obtained. To achieve this the time base circuit waits after each flyback until triggered by a pulse from the trigger circuit, and this pulse is not generated until the amplified signal reaches a value set by the *trigger* control. The number of complete input waveforms on the screen depends on the slope of the ramp, and this can be varied by the time base control. The last subsystem is the *power supply*, which must produce a low voltage to drive the other subsystems and a voltage of several thousand volts for the CRT. In many CROs there is a *bright line* facility which makes the next ramp trigger itself if the trigger control is turned to its zero. In other CROs the screen then becomes blank. In some

instruments the time base can be turned off and another signal applied directly to the X-plates.

2.16 Double-beam and dual-trace oscilloscopes

Sometimes it is very useful to be able to compare the input and output signals in a system. This can be done using two CROs, but it is then not possible to place one over the other or compare the phases. The double-beam instrument has two electron guns in its CRT, each with its own Y-plates but sharing X-plates. The cheaper dual-trace CRO (Figure 2.14) achieves much the same result by using a normal tube but switching its Y-plates rapidly between two Y-amplifiers. In either case two traces appear on the screen but the time base is triggered by only one of them.

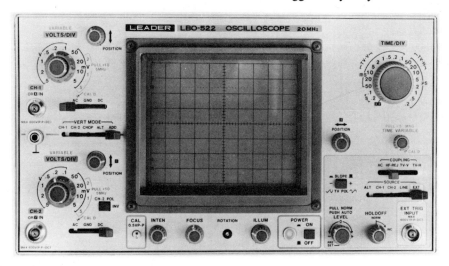

Figure 2.14 Dual-trace cathode ray oscilloscope

Summary

Moving-coil meter

The maximum current that a moving-coil meter can measure is called its full-scale deflection or FSD.

Moving-coil ammeter

Meter FSD is i, resistance of coil is r:

$$V = ir \qquad R = \frac{V}{I-i} = \frac{ir}{I-i}$$

Moving-coil voltmeter

Meter FSD is i, resistance of coil is r:

$$R + r = \frac{V}{i} \qquad R = \frac{V}{i} - r$$

ideal ammeter has zero resistance.
ideal voltmeter has infinite resistance.

The *quality of a voltmeter* can be measured by the fraction

$$\frac{\text{resistance of meter}}{\text{maximum voltage measured}} \ \Omega/V$$

which should be as large as possible.

Digital voltmeter

Has very high resistance, can be very accurate but is unsuitable for measuring varying voltages.

Ohmmeter

Measures resistance on a non-linear scale.

Cathode ray oscilloscope

- Plots voltage–time graphs for periodic voltages
- Measures DC and AC voltages
- Measures the period and frequency of AC signals.

Questions

1 A moving-coil meter of $100\,\mu A$ FSD has a resistance of $1000\,\Omega$. Describe how you would convert it to read (a) currents up to 5 A and (b) voltages up to 15 V. Calculate values for any components you would use.
 What would be the ohms/volt of of the voltmeter in (b)?

2 The diagram shows the circuit of an ohmmeter. The readings obtained from the 10 mA FSD meter when various resistors were connected between probes A and B are as follows:

Meter current (mA)	External resistance (Ω)
1.0	5400
2.0	2400
3.0	1400
4.0	900
5.0	600
7.1	250
8.0	150
8.6	100
9.2	50
9.8	10

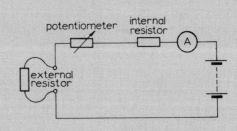

Describe the adjustments that should have been made before the readings were taken.

Plot a graph of meter reading (*y*) against resistance (*x*).

Use your graph to find the value of the resistor that would give a meter deflection of 3.5 mA and the meter reading produced by a resistor of 400 Ω resistance.

What is the total resistance of the fixed internal resistor, potentiometer and meter? What is the voltage of the battery?

3 Graphs (a), (b) and (c) represent traces on an oscilloscope screen when the *Y*-amplifier controls and time base controls are set to the values given below the diagrams. In each case find the peak-to-peak amplitude, the peak amplitude and if possible the RMS voltage of the signals. Measure also their periods and frequencies.

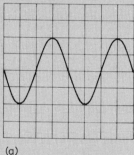

(a)

Y-amplifier 1 V/cm
timebase 5 ms/cm

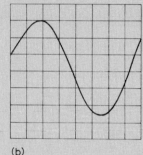

(b)

Y-amplifier 200 mV/cm
timebase 100 μs/cm

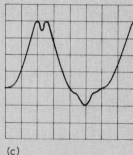

(c)

Y-amplifier 5 V/cm
timebase 20 μs/cm

4 A multimeter of 1 k Ω /V is set on its 10 V scale and used to measure the voltages across the resistors in the circuit shown.

What is the resistance of the multimeter?

What voltages will it read when connected across the resistors?

What would a digital multimeter read if used in the same way? Give your reasons.

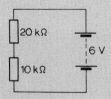

5 A moving-coil ammeter has a resistance of 5 Ω. It is used to measure the current flowing in the circuit shown. What will it read? What would an ideal ammeter read if used to measure this current?

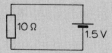

6 A moving-coil ammeter and voltmeter, both having a finite resistance, are to be used to measure the resistance of a resistor. The two circuits shown are suggested as ways of connecting the components.

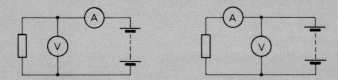

Compare the advantages and disadvantages of the use of the two circuits. Will either circuit give the correct answer? Give your reasons.

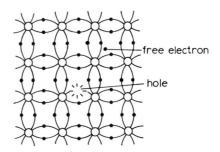

Semiconductor components

3.1 Semiconductor materials

Conductors and insulators were discussed in Chapter 1. You will remember that metals are conductors because their outer or *valence electrons* are free to move about inside the crystal lattice. The valence electrons of insulators require large amounts of extra energy if they are to break free from their atoms, and so at normal temperatures insulators do not conduct.

Semiconductors are insulators which require much less energy than normal for their electrons to break free, and so even at room temperatures there will be a few electrons able to carry an electric current through the material. When a valence electron leaves its atom in a metal the atom is left with a positive charge and is called an ion. The ion is fixed in the lattice and so can take no part in conduction. Ions produced in semiconductors have a strange property. The ion takes advantage of the relatively weak bond between valence electron and atom and steals an electron from a neighbour. This is repeated over and over again, so that the position of the atom that is an electron short moves about inside the lattice even though the atoms themselves are stationary. This peculiar behaviour deserves a special name, so the moving shortage of an electron is called a *hole* and can be thought of as a positive charge carrier free to move about inside the semiconductor. Obviously the value of the positive charge carried by a hole must be equal to the negative charge carried by an electron, and if a hole and an electron should ever meet the electron would drop into the hole and both would cease to exist. This is called *recombination*.

If you imagine a perfect crystal of semiconductor material with no other atoms present, then this is what is meant by an *intrinsic semiconductor*. A great deal of effort has gone into developing ways of growing such crystals. The most common semiconductor elements are *germanium* and *silicon*. Figure 3.1 shows a way of representing an intrinsic crystal of these materials in a diagram. The circles represent the atoms and the dots represent the valence electrons. Notice that one of the atoms has lost an electron, leaving a hole. The free electron is still present inside the crystal lattice, so that the crystal as a whole remains neutral.

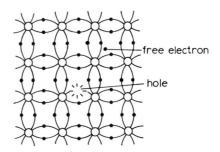

Figure 3.1   Intrinsic semiconductor crystal

Figure 3.2 shows a crystal of intrinsic semiconductor joined to the terminals of a battery. Electrons will be attracted to the positive terminal and so will flow in one direction, and holes will flow in the other direction towards the negative terminal. The total current in the circuit will be half 'electron current' and half 'hole current'.

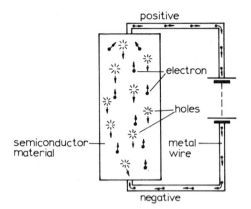

Figure 3.2   Conduction in an intrinsic semiconductor

In fact the current would be very small as at normal temperature few electron/hole pairs are formed. If however we supply energy by raising the temperature then more and more electrons will be able to escape from their atoms and the current will increase. If we think of the semiconductor crystal as a resistor then increasing its temperature reduces its resistance, which is the opposite to what happens in metals.

3.2 The thermistor

The *thermistor* is simply a semiconductor resistor used for its change in resistance with temperature as described in the previous section. Figure 3.3 shows some common forms and the symbol which can be used to represent them in circuit diagrams.

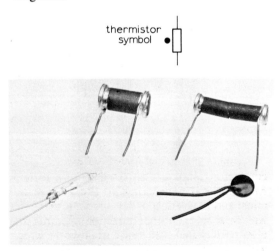

Figure 3.3   Thermistors

The thermistor is an example of a transducer; it converts changes in temperature to changes in resistance.

3.3 The light-dependent resistor

Heat is not the only way that energy can be supplied to a semiconductor. If light energy falls on a suitable semiconductor it produces hole/electron pairs and the resistance of the semiconductor falls. A component using this resistance change is called a *light-dependent resistor* or LDR (Figure 3.4). By far the most common example is the ORP 12. This has a resistance of 10 megohms in total darkness but only 100 ohms in bright sunlight. In normal room lighting the ORP 12 has a resistance of about 5 kilohms.

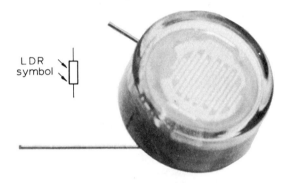

Figure 3.4   Light-dependent resistor

3.4 Extrinsic semiconductors

Even though intrinsic semiconductors have hole/electron pairs at room temperature, they are few in number and the material is a very poor conductor. It is possible to increase the conductivity to any value that may be required by adding a measured quantity of an impurity to the intrinsic crystal.

Both germanium and silicon have four valence electrons per atom, which allows each atom to join up with four other atoms within the crystal as shown in Figure 3.1. If an impurity with five valence electrons is added then one of the electrons will not be needed for bonding and will be free to move about the lattice as a conduction electron. The atom it comes from is not a semiconductor and so it leaves behind not a hole but a positive ion. The more impurity atoms are added, the more free electrons are produced and the greater the conductivity of the material. The semiconductor is now said to be *extrinsic* and is described as *N-type* semiconductor. The impurity is known as a *donor* impurity. The main carriers of electric current in an N-type semiconductor are electrons, and at the site of each of the impurity atoms there is a fixed positive ion.

The addition of an impurity is called *doping*. If the germanium or silicon is doped instead with an element having only three valence electrons in its atoms, an *acceptor* impurity, then the shortage of electrons produces holes in the material and negative ions. The result is *P-type* semiconductor.

The two types of semiconductor are shown in Figure 3.5.

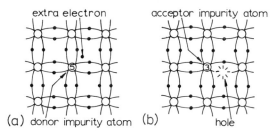

Figure 3.5 Extrinsic semiconductors (*a*) N-type (*b*) P-type

3.5 The junction diode

It is possible to dope a semiconductor crystal so that it is P-type at one end and N-type at the other, with a junction between the two kinds of material in the middle. Electrons in the N-type half are repelled away from the junction by the negative ions in the P-type region, and in the same way holes in the P-type are repelled by the positive ions in the N-type material. A space on either side of the junction is therefore left without either kind of charge carriers and is known as the *depletion layer*. This situation is shown in Figure 3.6.

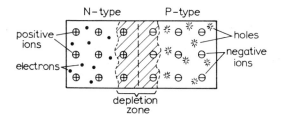

Figure 3.6 Depletion layer

Now suppose a battery of very small voltage was connected to the junction (Figure 3.7). In one direction it would attract the charge carriers away from the junction and make the depletion layer wider, and in the other it would repel the carriers and drive them towards the junction, so reducing the depletion layer. In neither case would any current flow because there is always some of the depletion layer remaining.

Now imagine the low-voltage battery replaced by one of higher voltage. In one direction there is still no current because the depletion layer is wider still, but in the other direction the layer disappears completely and current can flow.

A very useful device is now available which is an insulator in one direction and a conductor in the other, provided that the voltage applied to it is large enough. It is called a *diode* and is represented by the symbol in Figure 3.7. The current is conducted in the direction of the arrow.

Practical diodes come in many shapes and sizes depending on their intended use. Each diode has a maximum current rating, which if exceeded will cause overheating. It also has a peak inverse voltage (PIV), which is the maximum voltage that the diode can withstand in the reverse direction without conducting. Diodes with high current ratings are used as *rectifiers* (see Chapter 4) and are often of the 'top hat' shape. General-purpose diodes can carry currents of the order of 100 mA and look like very small resistors with a bar or line marked at one end. This end is the cathode and is the bar in the diode symbol, so that current is conducted towards this end. Figure 3.8 shows some of the common diodes that are available.

3.6 Diode characteristics

The exact way in which a diode behaves is best described by a graph of current against voltage, which is called the *characteristic* of the diode. The characteristics of three kinds of diode are shown in Figure 3.9.

The graphs are unusual in that they extend in both the positive and negative directions. The positive values are always measured with the diode connected so that it can conduct – *forward biased*. The diode is then reversed – *reverse biased* – and the currents and voltages plotted as negative. Figure 3.9 also gives characteristics for high and low resistances so that you can compare them with the diode characteristics.

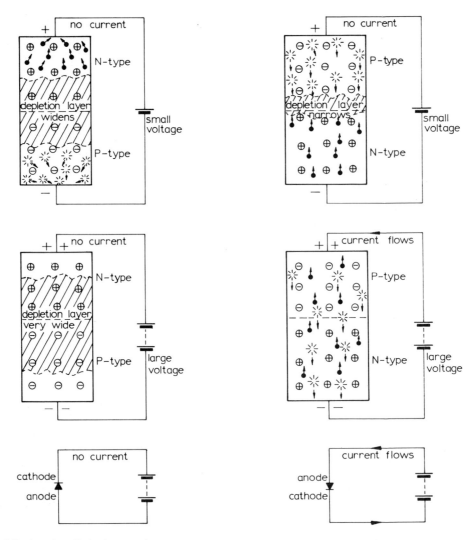

Figure 3.7   Junction diodes in operation

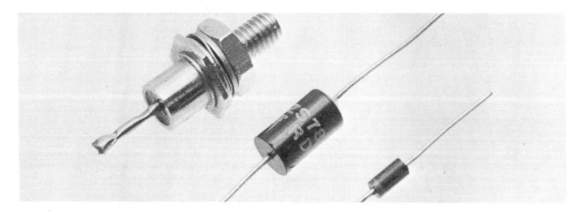

Figure 3.8   Some common diodes

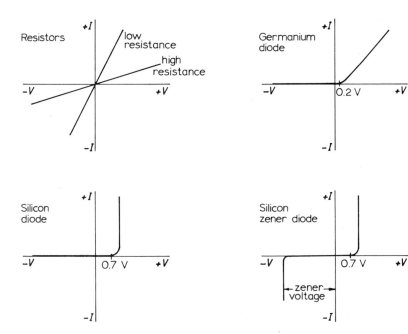

Figure 3.9 Diode characteristics

You will see that the positive and negative parts of the resistor characteristics are identical but that a diode resembles a very low resistance when forward biased and a very high resistance when reverse biased. This is what we would expect from the theory of the previous section, and this theory would also explain why the diodes do not conduct when forward biased until the voltage has risen some way above zero, namely 0.7 V for silicon and about 0.2 V for germanium. The ordinary germanium and silicon diodes have PIVs which are far larger than the values shown on the graphs and so they do not conduct in the reverse direction. The silicon *zener* diode is specially made so that it breaks down in the reverse direction at some particular voltage called its *zener voltage*. Zener diodes are manufactured in a range of voltages, and their use is described in Chapter 4.

The ohmmeter described in Chapter 2 provides us with a simple way of testing a diode. In one direction it will give a high resistance reading, and in the other a low reading.

3.7 The photodiode

The photodiode (Figure 3.10) is a normal junction diode with a transparent case or window. All diodes contain some hole/electron pairs at room temperatures and these give rise to a small current even when the diode is reverse biased. This current is called *leakage* and is normally only a few microamperes. However, when light falls on the junction the energy it contains produces a large number of extra hole/electron pairs and the leakage current is greatly increased. Photodiodes are used in preference to LDRs where the light intensity is changing rapidly and and an LDR would be too slow to follow it.

symbol

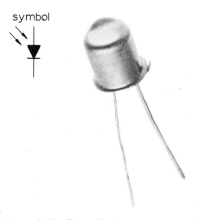

Figure 3.10 Photodiodes

3.8   The light-emitting diode

Light-emitting diodes (LEDs) (Figure 3.11) are manufactured from a semiconductor material that emits light when a current flows through the junction. The most common coloured light is red, but lower-brightness green and yellow LEDs are available. The voltage drop across a forward-biased LED is about 2 V, and above this voltage the current rapidly increases. A series resistor must be used to limit this current to about 10 milliamps or the junction will be destroyed. The value of this resistor can be calculated from:

$$R = \frac{\text{supply voltage} - 2}{0.01}\ \Omega$$

An LED and its series resistor can be used to replace a filament lamp, with the advantage that it uses less current, does not get hot and has no filament to burn out. The filament lamp is brighter, however, and emits white light.

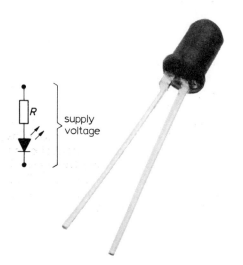

Figure 3.11   Light-emitting diode

3.9   The transistor

The *junction transistor* is a sandwich, either of P-type semiconductor between two slices of N-type (NPN transistor), or the reverse (PNP transistor) (Figure 3.12).

Transistors can be made of germanium or silicon, but by far the most common device is the silicon NPN transistor: the circuits in this book will be based on this type.

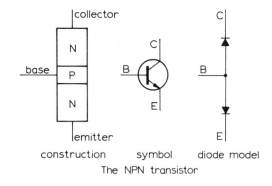

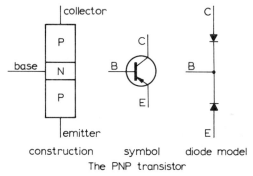

Figure 3.12   NPN and PNP transistors

Figure 3.13 shows an NPN transistor connected to two voltage sources S_1 and S_2. S_2 is fixed and could be a battery, but S_1 is variable from zero upward. The NPN regions are known as *emitter*, *base* and *collector*.

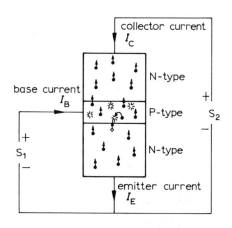

Figure 3.13   NPN transistor action

Starting with S_1 turned to zero and with reference to the diode model, you will see that no current can flow due to S_2 because the collector/base junction acts as a reverse-biased diode.

The voltage from S_1 is now gradually increased. As long as it is less than 0.7 V (assuming a silicon transistor) no current will flow into the base region because the depletion layer within the base/emitter diode will not have been removed. Above 0.7 V the base/emitter junction will act as a normal diode and electrons will flow from the emitter into the base. A few of these electrons will combine with the holes in the P region but most, particularly if the base region is thin, will be attracted by the positive of S_2 and continue on into the collector region and so through S_2 back to the emitter. The few lost by recombination in the base region are replaced from S_1 and so make up its current.

There are therefore two currents flowing at the same time. One flows round the circuit S_1 (base and emitter), and is called the *base current* I_B. The other flows round the circuit S_2 (collector, base and emitter), and is called the *collector current* I_C.

The emitter is in both circuits, and so the transistor is described as being in *common-emitter mode*. The value of the *emitter current* I_E is the sum of the other two currents:

$$I_E = I_B + I_C$$

Suppose that for every 100 electrons that entered the base region and passed on to the collector, there was one electron that recombined with a hole. This would mean that $I_C = 100 I_B$, and we would say that the transistor had a *common-emitter current gain* (usually just *gain*) of 100. The gain of a transistor is represented by h_{FE}, so that

$$I_C = h_{FE} I_B \qquad I_B = \frac{I_C}{h_{FE}} \qquad h_{FE} = \frac{I_C}{I_B}$$

The same equations can be applied to a PNP transistor, the only difference being that the polarity of the supplies have to be reversed.

A transistor can be tested using an ohmmeter. Connect between base and emitter, base and collector and emitter and collector in turn and in both directions. The diode models of the transistors will tell you what readings to expect.

3.10 The inverter circuit

The circuit of Figure 3.13 would be a disaster if it was actually used. As soon as the voltage of S_1 was a few millivolts above 0.7 V, the current into the base I_B would rapidly increase and the base/emitter diode would be destroyed. If the experimenter was very careful and was able to limit I_B to a safe value then I_C, which would always be a factor of h_{FE} larger than I_B, would become so large that the transistor would overheat and again be destroyed.

Resistors are needed in series with the base and the collector to protect them. The new circuit is shown in Figure 3.14 and is called an *inverter*. The reason for the name will become obvious later in the section. Note one or two changes. The voltage applied to the base is now called by its usual name, *input voltage* V_{IN}. The fixed voltage S_2 is now called the *supply voltage* V_{CC}.

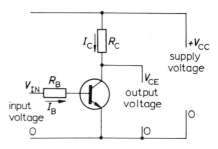

Figure 3.14 Inverter circuit

The equations of the previous section can be applied to the new circuit, and we can use them to construct some graphs.

First we have to decide on some resistor values, the gain of the transistor and the supply voltage. Suppose that the collector resistor R_C is 1 kΩ, the base resistor R_B is 10 kΩ and the supply voltage V_{CC} is 9 V, and assume that the transistor has $h_{FE} = 100$ (Figure 3.15).

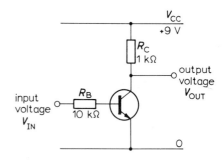

Figure 3.15 Practical inverter circuit

For the first calculation, $V_{IN} = 1$ V. The voltage across R_B is $V_{IN} - 0.7$. Using the values above,

$$I_B = \frac{V_{IN} - 0.7}{R_B} = \frac{1 - 0.7}{10} = 0.03 \text{ mA}$$

$$I_C = h_{FE} I_B = 100 \times 0.03 = 3 \text{ mA}$$

The voltage across R_C is $I_C R_C$, so that

$$V_{OUT} = V_{CC} - I_C R_C = 9 - (3 \times 1) = 6 \text{ V}$$

Example   *Here is one set of values for the circuit: when* $V_{IN} = 1$ *V,* $I_B = 0.03$ *mA,* $I_C = 3$ *mA and* $V_{OUT} = 6$ *V. What will these values be if* V_{IN} *is made 2 V?*

$$I_B = \frac{2 - 0.7}{10} = 0.13 \text{ mA}$$

$$I_C = 100 \times 0.13 = 13 \text{ mA}$$

$$V_{OUT} = 9 - (13 \times 1) = -4 \text{ V}$$

It is not possible to have a negative voltage, and so something must have gone wrong. The error is in the value of I_C. The transistor would like to pass 13 mA, but a supply of 9 V can only drive a current of 9 mA through a 1 kΩ resistor. The transistor would turn on as hard as it could so that no voltage was dropped across it, giving an output voltage of zero and a current of 9 mA.

The values are therefore:

$$V_{IN} = 2 \text{ V} \qquad I_B = 0.13 \text{ mA}$$

$$I_C = 9 \text{ mA} \quad V_{OUT} = 0 \text{ V}$$

Similar calculations could be carried out to produce a table of values such as the following, and these values can be used to plot a number of graphs as shown in Figure 3.16.

V_{IN} (volts)	I_B (mA)	I_C (mA)	V_{OUT} (volts)
0	0	0	9
0.3	0	0	9
0.5	0	0	9
0.7	0	0	9
1.0	0.03	3	6
1.3	0.06	6	3
1.5	0.08	8	1
1.7	0.1	9	0
2.0	0.13	9	0
2.5	0.18	9	0

Figure 3.16(a) shows a graph of I_C against I_B for the transistor. This is called its *transfer characteristic*. Without the collector resistor R_C the graph would continue as shown by the dotted line. During the horizontal part of the characteristic the transistor is *saturated*: that is, its resistance drops to zero and there is no voltage across it. The current is limited by the resistor R_C to V_{CC}/R_C.

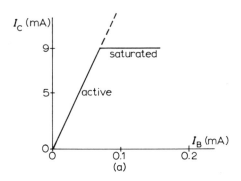

Figure 3.16(a)   Transfer characteristic

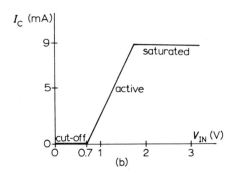

Figure 3.16(b) I_C against V_{IN}

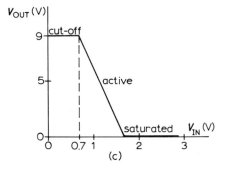

Figure 3.16(c)   Voltage characteristic

Figure 3.16(b) plots I_C against V_{IN}, and Figure 3.16(c) shows a *voltage characteristic* of V_{OUT} against V_{IN}. These two figures are placed one under the other so that it is possible to compare the values of I_C and V_{OUT} at a particular V_{IN}. Note that, as long as V_{IN} is less than 0.7 V, the collector current I_C is zero and the output voltage V_{OUT} is equal to the supply voltage. The transistor does not conduct in this region and is said to be *cut off*. During the sloping part of both graphs the transistor is in control of both I_C and V_{OUT}, but eventually it becomes saturated with the collector current maximum and the output voltage zero.

Consider the voltage characteristic. Three separate regions can be seen: transistor cut off, transistor active and the transistor saturated. The first and last give the circuit its name. When the input is a low voltage the output is high, and when the input is high the output is a low voltage.

3.11 The emitter-follower circuit

A transistor connected as an *emitter follower* is in *common-collector* mode. The common terminal is always the one connected to a supply rail. In this circuit it is the collector, and in the inverter circuit it was the emitter. In either case the common terminal is shared by the input and output circuits.

Consider how the output voltage V_{OUT} varies with the input voltage V_{IN}. If V_{IN} is below 0.7 V the transistor is cut off and V_{OUT} is zero. Once V_{IN} is above 0.7 V the base/emitter junction of the transistor acts like a forward-biased diode and drops a constant 0.7 V across it. V_{OUT} is therefore always 0.7 V lower than V_{IN}. In other words the output voltage *follows* the input voltage but 0.7 V behind. This characteristic of the circuit gives it its name. Figure 3.17 shows the voltage characteristic for the emitter follower.

Considering the circuit of Figure 3.17, and taking the supply voltage as 9 V and the gain of the transistor as 100, it is possible to calculate the base and collector currents for a particular value of V_{IN}. If $V_{IN} = 8$ V, $V_{OUT} = 8 - 0.7 = 7.3$ V, and the current through the 1 kΩ resistor would be 7.3 mA. This current is the emitter current I_E. Now $I_E = I_C + I_B$, and I_B is very small. I_E and I_C will therefore be very close in value and can be taken as equal: that is, $I_C = 7.3$ mA. $I_B = I_C/h_{FE}$, giving $I_B = 7.3/100 = 0.073$ mA.

Any circuit which applies 8 V to the input has to supply 0.073 mA. It is just as though the input was a resistor of $8/0.073 = 109.5$ k Ω. This imaginary resistance is called the *input resistance* of the circuit. All circuits with an input have an input resistance. We do not usually have to know input resistances very accurately, and it is good enough to use the equation:

emitter-follower input resistance

$= h_{FE}$ of transistor × emitter resistance.

The inverter has an input resistance equal to its base resistor R_B.

3.12 The Darlington pair

Transistors are available with common-emitter current gains (h_{FE}) from 10 to 1000, but sometimes even the highest gain is not enough. To obtain even larger gains, two transistors are connected together to form a *Darlington pair* (Figure 3.18).

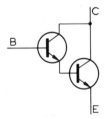

Figure 3.18 Darlington pair

The emitter current of the first transistor forms the base current of the second. Thus the base current of the first transistor is multiplied by the gains of the two transistors in turn, giving a total gain equal to the individual gains multiplied together:

$$\text{total gain} = h_{FE1}\, h_{FE2}$$

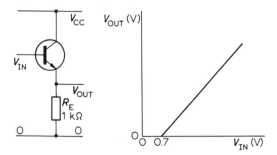

Figure 3.17 Emitter-follower circuit

Darlington transistors are available which consist of the two transistors connected as shown but contained in the same can so that they look like a single transistor.

When designing circuits using Darlingtons it is important to remember that they switch on at 1.4 V for V_{BE}, not 0.7 V.

3.13 The operational amplifier

This device is not a semiconductor *component*, but for convenience it is discussed in this chapter. In fact it consists of a transistor *circuit* of considerable complexity which has been found so useful that the whole circuit is manufactured on a single piece of silicon, fitted with input and output leads, and covered in plastic. It is our first *integrated circuit*, and can be treated just as if it were a new component. Figure 3.19 shows one of the most common *operational amplifiers* (opamp), the type 741, its connections, and the usual opamp symbol. You will notice that the symbol has only five connecting points but the actual 741 has eight pins. One is not used, and two can be used to set the output to an exact value and are not required for circuits in this book. These pins are labelled *offset null*.

Now for the operation of the operational amplifier. Two pins are marked *supply +* and *supply −* and these (as you would expect) are always connected to the positive and negative supply lines. The device also has two inputs, the *inverting input* (V_I) and the *non-inverting input* (V_N), and a single *output* (V_O). V_I, V_N and V_O are the values of the voltages applied to the inputs and obtained from the output. These voltages are joined by the equation:

$$V_O = A_O(V_N - V_I)$$

Here we have a slight problem. Voltages are measured between one point in a circuit and another. Usually one of the points is the negative or zero line. When we are calculating $V_N - V_I$ it does not matter where the reference point is as long as we use the same point for both voltages. When we obtain the output V_O we need to know the reference point used by the opamp. This is not the zero line but a voltage half-way between the positive supply and the zero line.

The other unknown quantity in the equation is A_O, the *open-loop voltage gain*. The open-loop voltage gain of an opamp is rather like the common-emitter current gain of a transistor. It is

a constant for a particular opamp, just as h_{FE} is constant for a particular transistor, but it is the ratio of two voltages instead of two currents. A 741 has an open-loop voltage gain of about 100 000.

An example will make the use of equation clear.

(a)

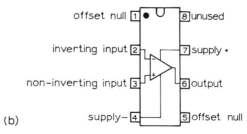

(b)

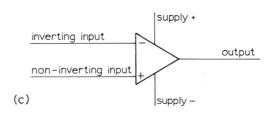

(c)

Figure 3.19(a) Type 741 operational amplifiers *(b)* Diagram for type 741 *(c)* Circuit symbol

Example *An opamp has an open-loop voltage gain of 400 and is connected between 12 V supply rails (Figure 3.20). Similar batteries are connected between the inputs and the zero line, but the one connected to the inverting input has a voltage of 5.88 V and the one connected to the non-inverting* *input has a voltage of only 5.87 V. What will be the voltage at the output with respect to the zero line? What would it be if the batteries were exchanged?*

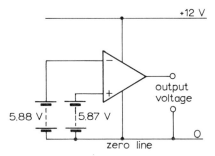

Figure 3.20

From the question,

$$V_I = 5.88 \text{ V}$$

$$V_N = 5.87 \text{ V}$$

$$A_O = 400$$

Using the equation $V_O = A_O(V_N - V_I)$,

$$V_O = 400(5.87 - 5.88)$$

$$= 400(-0.01)$$

$$= -4 \text{ V}$$

This voltage is relative to a point half-way between $+12$ V and zero, that is 6 V. The output voltage is therefore 4 V *below* 6 V, or 2 V.

If the batteries were exchanged then

$$V_O = 400(5 \times 88 - 5 \times 87)$$

$$V_O = 4 \text{ V}$$

The output is therefore $4 + 6 = 10$ V relative to the zero line.

In the example the opamp had an open-loop gain of 400. This is very low for a modern opamp. A more sensible value would be 100 000. What would be the output voltages if an opamp of this gain had been used?

If you substitute into the equation you will obtain values for V_O of -1000 V and 1000 V. That is, the output voltage relative to the zero line should be -994 V and 1006 V. In reality the output is limited by the supply, and so the -994 volts will actually be 0 V and 1006 volts will be 12 V.

In general we can say that:

If V_I is greater than V_N the output goes to the negative or zero supply line.
If V_N is greater than V_I the output goes to the positive supply line.

This is true unless the two inputs are very nearly equal, when we must use the equation. If they are exactly equal the output will be half-way between the supply lines.

A disadvantage in the 741 opamp is that its output cannot get closer than about 2 V to either supply rail. Using a 12 V supply its maximum output voltage would be 10 V and its minimum 2 V.

If you find the idea of a voltage relative to the mid voltage difficult you are not alone, and a way round it has been devised. Instead of a single battery to provide the supply, two are used. They are connected as shown in Figure 3.21, and the junction between them is called zero volts and marked with an earth or ground symbol. All voltages, including the output, are relative to this point. This arrangement is called a *dual power supply* and is very common where opamps are used.

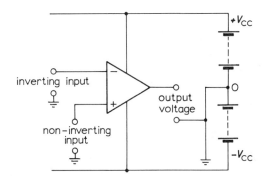

Figure 3.21   Dual power supply

Summary

Intrinsic semiconductor

A very pure sample of semiconductor crystal.

Extrinsic semiconductor

A sample of semiconductor which has been doped with an impurity.

N-type semiconductor has been doped with a *donor* impurity which adds conduction electrons but leaves the semiconductor electrically neutral.

P-type semiconductor has been doped with an *acceptor* impurity which adds conduction holes but leaves the semiconductor electrically neutral.

Thermistor   ### Light-dependent resistor

The resistance decreases as the temperature rises.

The resistance decreases as the light intensity increases

Junction diode   ### Zener diode

Conducts only in the direction of the arrow. Silicon drops 0.7 V across it when forward biased.

Insulating property breaks down when reverse biased at a predetermined zener voltage.

Light-emitting diode   ### Photodiode

Emits light when a current is passed through it in the forward direction.

Resistance when reverse biased; falls when it is illuminated.

The transistor

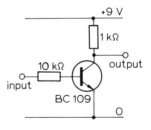

C collector; E emittor, B base.

$$I_C + I_B = I_E \qquad h_{FE} = \frac{I_C}{I_B}$$

Basic circuits

Transistor invertor

+9 V
1 kΩ
10 kΩ
output
input
BC 109

The output voltage is equal to the supply voltage as long as the input voltage is below 0.7 V. If the input rises much above this voltage, the output falls to zero.

Emitter-follower driver

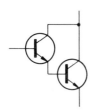

The output is always 0.7 V below the input voltage.

$$\text{input current} = \frac{\text{output current}}{h_{FE}}$$

The operational amplifier

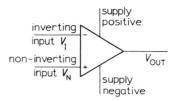

The circuit amplifies the difference between the two voltages at the inputs.

$$V_{OUT} = A_O(V_N - V_I)$$

A_O is called the open-loop voltage gain

Common opamp: type 741
Improved opamp: type 3140

The Darlington pair

A single transistor can be replaced by two transistors joined together, giving an h_{FE} equal to the product of the individual gains.

Questions

1 'An extrinsic semiconductor contains negative electrons or positive holes and yet is electrically neutral.' Explain why this is so.

2 An electronic thermometer consists of a probe fixed to a box on which is mounted a moving-coil meter and an on/off switch. Suggest a circuit for the device and explain how it would work.

3 Early germanium diodes were encapsulated in glass and painted black. If the paint was scraped off it was found that they conducted slightly when reverse biased and that this leakage current varied with light intensity. Explain this.

4 An LED is to be used to indicate when a 12 V supply is switched on. The diode drops a voltage of 2 V across it when it carries the required current of 20 mA.
   Calculate the value of the series resistor and explain why such a resistor is needed.

5 A ohmmeter was used to measure the resistance between the leads of three transistors—1, 2 and 3. The results were simply classified as high or low and recorded in the table below. Complete the table and give as much information as you can about the transistors.

Base/collector		Base/emitter		Collector/emitter	
+ to B	+ to C	+ to B	+ to E	+ to C	+ to E
1 high	low			high	high
2 low		low	high	high	
3 low	low	high			low

6 A transistor inverter has a collector resistor R_c of 3.9 kΩ, a base resistor R_B of 27 kΩ, includes a transistor of h_{FE} equal to 100 and operates from a 12 V supply. If the input voltage is 2 V, calculate

(a) The PD across the 27 kΩ resistor.
(b) The current in the 27 kΩ resistor (I_B)
(c) The current in the 3.9 kΩ resistor (I_C).
(d) The output voltage.

The transistor is now replaced by one with a different h_{FE} and an input of 2 V is found to give an output of 3 V. What is the h_{FE} of the new transistor?

7 The resistance of a thermistor is found to vary linearly over the range 20 °C to 90 °C, being 150 kΩ at the lower temperature and 10 kΩ at the higher. The thermistor is used in the circuit shown. The common-emitter current gain (h_{FE}) for the transistor is 50. Construct a table with columns for temperature, base current I_B, collector current I_C and output voltage V_{OUT}, and use it to draw graphs of I_B, I_C and V_{OUT} against temperature.

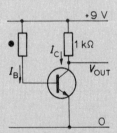

8 An emitter-follower driver is used to drive a current through a 6 V, 100 mA lamp. Draw the circuit used, and calculate the current in the lamp when input voltage is 4 V. If the transistor has $h_{FE} = 200$, calculate the input current.

9 Use the graph shown to find the h_{FE} of the transistor and the value of R_C.

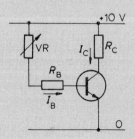
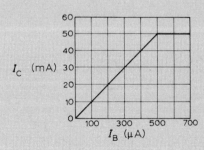

4

Voltage sources

Two kinds of voltage source will be considered in this chapter: those that provide the power to operate the circuits, and those that provide the input voltages.

4.1 Batteries

Batteries consisting of a number of *dry cells*, each of 1.5 volts, connected in series provide a convenient source of power for many circuits. Their main advantage is that they are portable and they are the usual choice if the circuit is to be used out of doors. The PD between the terminals of a battery is called its *electromotive force* (EMF), and has its greatest value when the battery is new. The chemicals inside the battery offer resistance to the flow of current, and the resistance between its terminals is called its *internal resistance*. The internal resistance of a new battery is at its lowest value, and increases as the battery is used. At the same time the EMF decreases, and both effects combine to reduce the maximum current that the battery can supply.

The circuit diagram in Figure 4.1 shows a battery of X volts EMF and internal resistance r ohms connected to a resistor of resistance R ohms. The voltmeter in the circuit will measure both the voltage across the resistor and the voltage between the terminals of the battery, as in this circuit they are the same. This voltage V will be less than X because some of X will be used to drive a current through the internal resistance.

The lost voltage $X - V = Ir$, where I is the current in the circuit in amperes. The value of I can be calculated by using the Ohm's law equation on the whole circuit or just on resistor R:

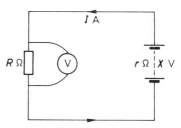

Figure 4.1 Battery internal resistance

$$I = \frac{X}{R + r} \qquad \text{or} \qquad I = \frac{V}{R}$$

If the value of R is slowly increased from zero the current decreases from its maximum value given by $I = X/r$. When R is zero, all the power produced by the battery is wasted as heat inside the battery. As R rises, some power will still be wasted but there will also be I^2R watts of useful power produced in the resistor. The battery is supplying power more efficiently. The useful power will increase until the external resistance is equal to the internal resistance of the battery: $R = r$. V is then exactly half of X and the useful and wasted powers are equal. The efficiency is now 50%. Further increase of R reduces the output power but increases the efficiency, until when the output current has been reduced to zero the efficiency is 100%.

It is worth looking at the performance of a battery in some detail, as all other voltage sources behave in the same way. If we want maximum power transferred the external load must equal the source resistance, but if we want greater efficiency the external load should be as large as possible. In electronics we are usually more concerned with efficiency than maximum power.

4.2   Rechargeable batteries

The nickel-cadmium (nicad) cell with an EMF of 1.25 volts is an alternative to the dry cell in portable equipment. Unlike the dry cell, the nicad can be recharged when exhausted using a mains-powered charger, and although they are expensive to buy these batteries are cheaper than dry cells in the long run.

4.3   The mains power supply

The cheapest source of electrical power is the mains, and so whenever possible it is used to power electronic circuits. Any mains power supply must perform at least three operations.

● The 240 volt mains must be *transformed* to a suitable voltage.

● The alternating supply must be *rectified* so that the current flows in only one direction.

● Variations in the rectified voltage must be *smoothed* out.

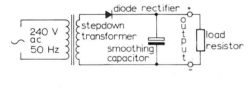

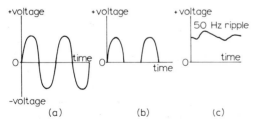

Figure 4.2   Mains power supply (*a*) Alternating voltage (*b*) Half-wave rectified voltage (*c*) Direct voltage with 50Hz ripple

The circuit diagram in Figure 4.2 shows the most simple arrangement that can carry out these three operations. The three graphs show (a) the shape of the alternating voltage as it leaves the transformer, (b) the voltage after being rectified by the diode, and (c) the voltage after the capacitor has smoothed out most of the variations. What is left is called *ripple*. The frequency of the ripple is the same as that of the mains, 50 hertz.

When a single diode is used as a rectifier it produces *half-wave rectification*, and half of the output from the transformer is wasted. Figure 4.3 shows a power supply using four diodes to form a *diode bridge*, which routes both halves of the alternating cycle into the same direction so that neither is lost. The graph shows the result, which is known as *full-wave rectification*. Once again this can be smoothed by a capacitor, but this time any remaining ripple will have a frequency of twice the mains frequency or 100 hertz.

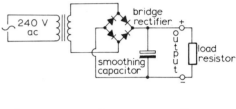

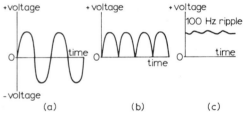

Figure 4.3   Diode bridge circuit (*a*) Alternating voltage (*b*) Full-wave rectified voltage (*c*) Direct voltage with 100 Hz ripple

The graphs of the smoothed output show that the direct output voltage is nearly equal to the peak value of the output from the transformer. A 6 volt mains transformer may therefore give an output of 6 volts RMS, and so we could expect a DC voltage across the capacitor and load of ($\sqrt{2}$)6 or 8.5 volts. In fact it will be 0.7 volts less than this in a half-wave circuit and 1.4 volts less in a full-wave circuit, owing to the voltage drop across the rectifier diodes.

When designing power supplies the main consideration is for safety both of the components and the user. The safety of the components can be ensured by using transformers and diodes that have a maximum current-carrying capacity of twice the current you need. The peak input voltage of the diodes and the voltage rating of the capacitor should also be at least twice the peak voltage from the transformer.

To protect the user the primary of the transformer must be connected to the mains by a main lead fitted with a cable clamp at the transformer end and a mains plug containing a suitable low-current fuse at the other end. Do not use the 13 A fuse that came with the plug. The *earth* wire of the cable should be connected to the iron core of the transformer and to the case of the power supply if this is metal. Should a live wire come loose and touch the case the circuit will be completed to earth and the fuse in the plug will melt. In an emergency it would be vital to disconnect the power supply from the mains as quickly as possible, and just pulling out the plug might be difficult if it was a long way away. A double-pole switch should be fitted between the cable clamp

and the transformer primary. It is also useful to be able to see when the circuit is switched on, and this is best achieved by connecting a *neon indicator* with a series resistor of 100 kilohms in parallel to the primary coil.

When the power supply is in use a component may fail in the circuit that it is powering which would cause a short circuit between the positive and negative rails. The supply would then try to provide a very large current which could damage the transformer secondary or the diodes. The simple way to prevent this is to include a fuse in the positive supply lead. Another solution is the use of an electromechanical or temperature-sensitive *overload trip* which would disconnect the supply at some current level.

Figure 4.4 shows a power supply incorporating these improvements.

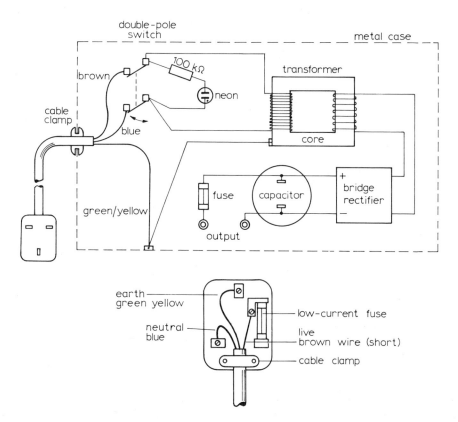

Figure 4.4 Power supply and plug

4.4   Load regulation in a power supply

As the load resistance of a power supply is reduced, the current taken from the supply increases and the voltage at its output falls. This fall is the result of the resistance of the components in the power supply, chiefly the transformer secondary, and the effect is exactly the same as was found in batteries due to their internal resistance. A power supply in which the output voltage falls rapidly as the output current increases would be said to have poor *load regulation* and would be unsatisfactory in use. To overcome poor load regulation a number of regulating or *stabilizing* circuits have been invented which, when connected across the output of an unregulated power supply, give a constant voltage output.

4.5   The zener diode stabilizer

In Chapter 3 it was described how, when an increasing voltage was applied in the reverse direction to it, a zener diode suddenly started to conduct at a particular zener voltage. Suppose the circuit for Figure 4.5 was to be used to provide a 5 V stabilized supply capable of a 100 mA maximum output current from an unstabilized supply. Tests would be carried out on the unstabilized supply to measure the output voltage when the output current was 100 mA. We will assume the result to be 8 V. The diode must have a zener voltage of 5 V and be capable of carrying a current of at least 100 mA. The limiting resistor can now be calculated. At 100 mA the voltage across it will be $8 - 5 = 3$ V and so $R = 3/0.1 = 30 \ \Omega$. When the output current is less than 100 mA the excess will flow to earth through the zener (Figure 4.5).

This circuit has the advantage that it is simple, and it has a measure of current overload protection because the output current is always limited by the limiting resistor. Unfortunately the circuit is wasteful because the 100 mA is always flowing whether needed or not. This might not matter for small currents, but it would be unsatisfactory for currents of several amperes. A transistor in common-collector (emitter-follower) mode can be added to the circuit as in Figure 4.6, when the main current will be carried by the transistor but the output voltage will be maintained at 0.7 V below the zener voltage.

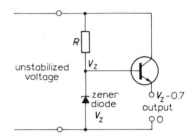

Figure 4.6   Modified stabilizer circuit

The transistor used would be a power type and, as the gain of power transistors tends to be low, a normal transistor is often connected to it to form a Darlington pair. Another modification is to add a potentiometer across the zener so that a variable output voltage can be obtained. Both modifications are included in Figure 4.7.

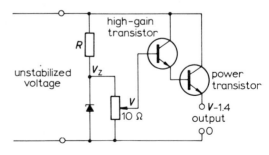

Figure 4.7   Stabilizer circuit with Darlington pair and potentiometer

Better stabilization can be obtained by comparing the output of the power supply with the

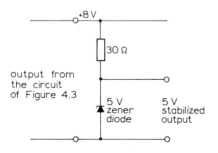

Figure 4.5   Zener diode stablizer

voltage from the zener and continually altering the output until they are equal. The operational amplifier is ideally suited to do this. The zener voltage is supplied to the non-inverting input and the output fed back to the inverting input of the operational amplifier (Figure 4.8). If the voltage at the inverting input is lower than that at the non-inverting input, the output of the opamp will rise. As the opamp is connected to the base of the emitter follower, the output voltage of the power supply will rise as well. A similar action will take place if the output is too high, and so the output voltage is held constant regardless of the load. This is an example of *negative feedback*. A potential divider can be used to make this kind of power supply variable if required.

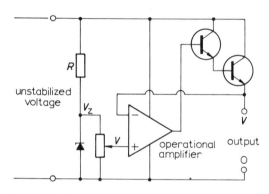

Figure 4.8 Stabilizer circuit with operational amplifier

A simple way of obtaining a stabilized supply now available is the use of a *voltage regulator*. This is an integrated circuit which contains the zener, opamp, output transistor and some extra circuitry which protects the output against overload currents, all for the price of the zener and transistor. Figure 4.9 shows the circuit used with a typical regulator.

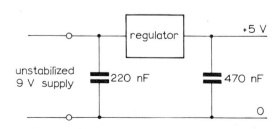

Figure 4.9 Circuit with regulator

4.6 The potential divider

Consider the circuit of Figure 4.10. The two resistors P and Q are in series and so they carry the same current. The value of the current is given by

$$I = \frac{V}{P+Q}$$

We can now apply the equation $V = IR$ to each of the resistors in turn to calculate the voltage across it.

$$\text{voltage across } P = \frac{PV}{P+Q}$$

$$\text{voltage across } Q = \frac{QV}{P+Q}$$

The voltages are in the same ratio as the resistances. This may look complicated when written as equations, but is simple when applied to an example.

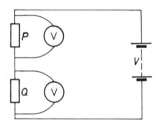

Figure 4.10

Example   *Resistors of resistance* 3 kΩ *and* 1 kΩ are connected across the terminals of a 12 V battery (Figure 4.11). What is the voltage across each resistor?

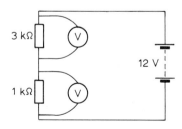

Figure 4.11

The total resistance is $3+1 = 4$ kΩ.
The current in the circuit is $I = 12/4 = 3$ mA.

The voltage across the 3 kΩ resistor is 3×3 = 9 V.
The voltage across the 1 kΩ resistor is 3×1 = 3 V.
Note that the voltage must add up to the supply voltage.

In the example the three units volts, kilohms and milliamperes were used together. This combination is very useful in electronics.

Example   *Two resistors are connected in series between a power rail at +6 V and earth. The upper resistor has a resistance of 2.7 kΩ and the voltage at the junction of the resistors is 1.5 V (Figure 4.12). What must be the resistance of the lower resistor?*

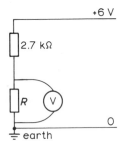

Figure 4.12

Power rails are a useful idea to simplify circuits. They are just like the conducting wires of the previous example with the battery left out. All voltages are measured relative to the lower power rail, which is called earth, ground or the zero line. You imagine that the negative terminal of any voltmeter is connected to this line.

The statement that the voltage at the junction is 1.5 V means that there is a voltage of 1.5 V across the lower resistor R. Therefore there must be a voltage of $6 - 1.5 = 4.5$ V across the 2.7 kΩ resistor.

The current in the 2.7 kΩ resistor is $4.5/2.7$ = 1.7 mA. This current also flows through R, so

$$R = \frac{1.5}{1.7} = 0.9 \text{ k}\Omega = 900 \text{ }\Omega$$

Example   *A potential divider consists of a variable resistor and two resistors connected between 9 V power rails as shown in Figure 4.13.*

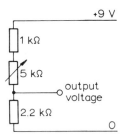

Figure 4.13

How will the voltage at the output vary as the variable resistor is turned from its maximum value to zero?

When the potentiometer is set to its maximum of 5 kΩ the resistance above the output is 6 kΩ and below is 2.2 kΩ. Using the potential divider equation, the voltage across the 2.2 kΩ resistor, and so the output voltage is,

$$\frac{2.2 \times 9}{2.2 + 6} = 2.4 \text{ V}$$

When the potentiometer is set to zero the voltage is

$$\frac{2.2 \times 9}{2.2 + 1} = 6.2 \text{ V}$$

As the potentiometer is turned from maximum to minimum, the output voltage rises from 2.4 V to 6.2 V.

The last example is particularly important because in practical circuits a potential divider is often used with a semiconductor transducer such as an LDR or thermistor instead of the variable resistor. This acts in the same way, with the output voltage increasing as the light intensity or temperature increases. In fact the potential divider with a transducer as one of its resistors is important enough to be considered as one of our basic circuits. Figure 4.14 shows two versions. In (a) the voltage at the junction rises when the resistance of the transducer is reduced, and in (b) it falls.

4.7   A light unit

This is a basic circuit consisting of a transducer and a resistor as described in the previous section (Figure 4.15). The transducer is an LDR (Section

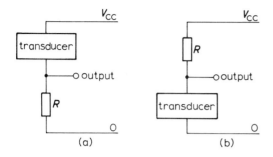

Figure 4.14 Potential dividers with transducers

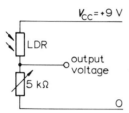

Figure 4.15

3.3) and it forms the upper half of the potential divider. If the intensity of the light falling upon the LDR increases, the resistance of the LDR will fall. The output voltage from the potential divider will therefore rise. The potential divider will give the greatest change in output voltage when the resistances of the LDR and lower resistor are equal, and the resistor is made variable so that this can be achieved. By adjusting the potentiometer it is possible to operate the circuit successfully over a wide range of light intensities.

4.8   A heat unit

One again a potential divider is used with a transducer as the upper resistor, but this time the transducer is a thermistor (Section 3.2). As the temperature of the thermistor rises so too does the output voltage of the circuit (see Figure 4.16). The resistor is a potentiometer connected as a variable resistor to allow for different temperature ranges.

In spite of the similarities in their circuits, the light unit and the heat unit are very different to use as a parts of a system. The resistance of an LDR varies from nearly infinity in the dark to a few hundred ohms in a good light. When the

LDR resistance is infinite, the output voltage will be close to zero, and when it is at its lowest the voltage will approach V_{CC}. This very large range in output voltages makes light-operated systems easy to design.

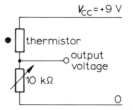

Figure 4.16

The resistance of a thermistor falls by no more than a factor of ten, which produces an output voltage change of only a few volts. This makes the design of the next stage in the system much more critical.

4.9   The time delay unit

In this basic circuit the lower part of a potential divider is a capacitor and the upper is a resistor (Figure 4.17). As long as the switch across the capacitor is held closed, the output voltage will be zero. Once the switch is released the capacitor will begin to charge through the fixed and variable resistors as described in Section 1.14, and the output voltage will rise according to the graph of Figure 1.15a. With the variable resistor set to its maximum the time constant will be

$$101\,000 \times \frac{220}{1\,000\,000} = 22 \text{ seconds}$$

The output voltage will therefore take 22 seconds to reach 6 volts and 66 seconds to reach 9 volts. Reducing the variable resistor reduces the time constant.

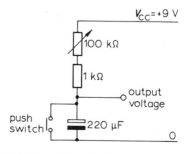

Figure 4.17   Time delay circuit

4.10   The rule of ten

The potential divider can be used to obtain a lower voltage than that provided by the supply. Once the lower voltage is obtained it will normally be used to drive another circuit, which at its most simple could be another resistor.

Example   *A potential divider made up of two 100 Ω resistors is connected to a 6 V supply and the output used to drive a current through a 1 kΩ resistor (Figure 4.18). What will be the output voltage?*

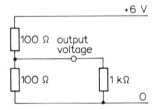

Figure 4.18

If we just applied the potential divider theory to the two 100 Ω resistors we would expect the output voltage to be 3 V:

$$\frac{100 \times 6}{100 + 100} = 3$$

In this case, however, the lower resistor has a 1 kΩ resistor in parallel to it, and to find the total we must use the parallel resistor equation:

$$\frac{1}{R} = \frac{1}{100} + \frac{1}{1000} = \frac{11}{1000}$$

$$R = \frac{1000}{11} = 90.9 \ \Omega$$

Applying the potential divider equation, the output voltage is

$$\frac{90.9 \times 6}{90.9 + 100} = 2.85 \text{ V}$$

This is not far from the 3 V obtained by ignoring the load.

Example   *The load resistor in the previous example is changed from 1 kΩ to 50 Ω.*

$$\frac{1}{R} = \frac{1}{100} + \frac{1}{50} = \frac{3}{100}$$

$$R = \frac{100}{3} = 33.3 \ \Omega$$

The output voltage is

$$\frac{33.3 \times 6}{33.3 + 100} = 1.5 \text{ V.}$$

This time the output voltage is much lower than the output from the potential divider unloaded.

These examples show that as the load resistor becomes smaller the output voltage becomes lower. The first of the examples shows that the smallest load resistance that gives an output which is near to the unloaded value is one that is ten times the value of the resistors used in the potential divider. This can be taken as generally true, and leads to the *rule of ten*:

The load resistance connected to a potential divider must be at least ten times the value of the resistors used in the potential divider.

If the resistors in the potential divider are not equal it is best to make the load resistance ten times the larger.

4.11   The potentiometer as a potential divider

There is often the need to obtain a variable voltage from a fixed voltage. If the ends of a potentiometer's track are connected across the fixed voltage, a variable voltage can be obtained from the slider. When used in this way the slider divides the potentiometer track into two resistances in series and so forms a potential divider. The three circuit diagrams in Figure 4.19 show (a) the potentiometer alone when the output voltage varies from 0 to 6 volts, (b) the potentiometer combined with a fixed resistor giving a voltage range from 0 to 3 volts, and (c) a circuit giving a range from 3 volts to 6 volts.

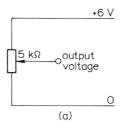

(a)

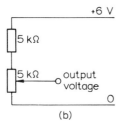

(b)

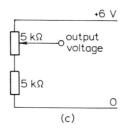

(c)

Figure 4.19 Potentiometer as potential divider

4.12 Signal generators and function generators

Many of the circuits to be studied in the next chapter need an alternating voltage as input. When the circuits are in use, this voltage is usually provided by a transducer of some kind. However, when they are being tested it is very useful to be able to apply an alternating voltage to their input which can be varied in frequency and amplitude.

The *signal generator* provides such a voltage (Figure 4.20). It consists of an alternating voltage generator called an *oscillator* followed by a potentiometer connected as a potential divider so that the amplitude can be varied. Like any potential divider the rule of ten must be used if the signal generator's output is used to drive other circuits. Most signal generators use a potentiometer of 600 ohms (or a circuit which behaves as if it was a 600 ohm potentiometer), and we must make sure that the resistance of the circuit they are to drive is at least ten times this value.

Figure 4.20 Signal generator

Some signal generators have a second output with an output resistance of only 3 or 4 ohms so that they can drive low-resistance transducers like loudspeakers directly.

All signal generators produce a sine-wave output and some can produce a square wave as well. Some have a potential divider made up of fixed resistors to reduce their output still further, for testing circuits that require a very small input voltage. These resistors are calculated so that the voltage can be reduced by factors of ten, and are called *attenuators*.

Function generators are similar to signal generators but they usually provide more types of wave, such as triangle or sawtooth waveforms.

Summary

Mains power supply

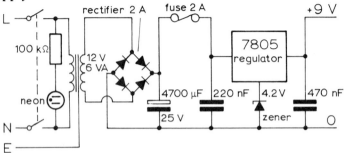

If the 4.2 V zener is replaced by a wire, the output becomes 5 V. For output voltages above 5 V use resistor R where

$$R = \frac{V-5}{1.5}\,k\Omega$$

V is the required voltage.

Battery power supply

All batteries have internal resistance, and if they are to be used to power your circuit remember that the circuit must have a resistance much larger than the internal resistance of the battery.

The larger a battery the lower its resistance, and so it is wise to use the largest battery that the conditions of size and cost will allow.

Basic circuits

Some input circuits follow that are based on the potential divider.

Voltage unit

Gives a voltage which increases from zero to 9 V as the potentiometer slider is moved from bottom to top.

Light unit

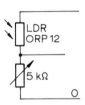

Gives a voltage which increases as the ORP 12 (light-dependent resistor) is illuminated more brightly. The potentiometer allows for different light intensities.

Heat unit

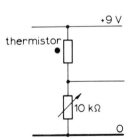

Gives a voltage which increases as the temperature of the thermistor is raised. The potentiometer varies the actual voltage at a particular temperature.

Time delay

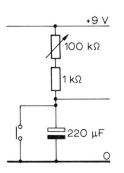

+9 V

100 kΩ

1 kΩ

220 μF

Gives a voltage which rises at a rate depending on the setting of the potentiometer once the switch is opened.

Zener diode

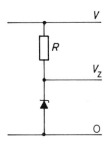

The diode breaks down in the reverse-biased direction at zener voltage V_z. Protective resistor R is required:

$$R = \frac{V - V_z}{I}$$

where I is the standing current.

Potential divider theory

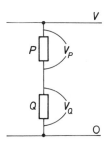

Voltage across P:

$$V_P = \frac{PV}{P + Q}$$

Voltage across Q:

$$V_Q = \frac{QV}{P + Q}$$

$$\frac{V_P}{V_Q} = \frac{P}{Q}$$

$$V_P + V_Q = V$$

Rule of ten

The load resistance connected to a potential divider must be at least ten times the value of the resistors used in the potential divider.

The signal generator, oscillator or function generator

Any of these instruments can be used as a source of alternating voltage of variable amplitude and frequency.

Questions

1 A battery has an EMF of 9 V and an internal resistance of 1.5 Ω. A variable resistor is connected across the terminals of the battery. What current will flow in the circuit when the resistor is set to (a) 10 Ω (b) 1.5 Ω and (c) 0.5 Ω?

In each case calculate the PD across the resistor, the power developed in the resistor and the power wasted inside the battery.

2 A cell can supply a current of 0.6 A through a 2 Ω resistor but only 0.2 A through a 7 Ω resistor. What are the EMF and the internal resistance of the cell?

3 A voltmeter of resistance 50 Ω is used to measure the EMF of a 12 V battery which has an internal resistance of 15 Ω. What will the voltmeter read?

The experiment is repeated with a voltmeter of 150 resistance. What will be the new value for the EMF?

Is it possible to measure the EMF of a battery with a moving-coil voltmeter?

4 A 5 kΩ and a 10 kΩ resistors are connected in series to a 9 V battery which has negligible internal resistance. What will be the voltage across the 10 kΩ resistor?

5 Calculate the voltage across the resistor Q in the following circuits:

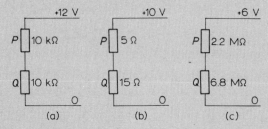

(a)   (b)   (c)

6 Calculate the voltage at A relative to the zero line in the following circuits:

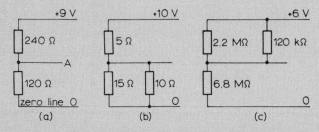

(a)   (b)   (c)

7 Sketch a graph of voltage at A relative to earth (*y*-axis) against the resistance of the potentiometer between its slider and earth as the slider is moved from the bottom to the top of its track.

8 Design a potential divider that will supply a 4.5 V motor from a 12 V battery of negligible internal resistance. The current taken by the motor varies between 5 mA and 800 mA.

9 Design a circuit for Question 8 which uses a resistor and a zener diode. In what way is this circuit superior to the simple potential divider using resistors?

10 Draw circuits showing how a voltmeter could be made to measure (a) temperature (b) light intensity (c) time intervals.

11 The high resistance voltmeter in the circuit shown reads 5 V. Calculate the current in each resistor and the value of R.

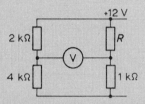

12 Sketch a graph of output voltage against slider position measured from A as the slider is moved from A to B.

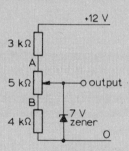

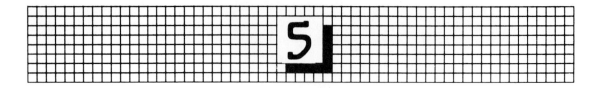

5

Basic switch circuits

Electronic switch circuits are so called because their action is similar to that of a mechanical switch. A study of these devices will form the first part of the chapter.

5.1 Mechanical switches

Electrical current can only flow if there is a complete circuit, and it is the job of a switch to substitute an insulator for part of the conducting path so that the current is stopped. The most simple type would be a lever which could move a piece of metal across a gap in the circuit, and the switch symbol is a diagram of this. In real switches the metal that bridges the gap is usually spring loaded, so that when the operating lever or *toggle* is moved at first nothing happens and then the switch action takes place very rapidly into its closed position. A similar fast switching action takes place when the toggle is moved in the opposite direction and the switch breaks the circuit.

The basic characteristic of a toggle switch is therefore a fast switch between two stable states, on and off, and this is also the characteristic of electronic switch circuits.

A toggle switch of the type described would be called a single-*pole*, single-*throw* (SPST) switch.

single pole,
single throw

single pole,
double throw

double pole,
single throw

double pole,
double throw

four pole, three way

Figure 5.1 Mechanical switches

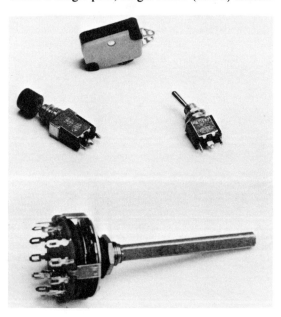

Many switches move the pole between two fixed contacts as shown in the second diagram of Figure 5.1. The switch would then be described as a single-pole, double-throw (SPDT) switch or as a single-pole *changeover* switch. A single toggle can be made to move two poles at the same time, leading to double-pole, single-throw (DPST) and double-pole, double-throw (DPDT) switches.

The toggle lever is not the only way to operate a switch, and the lever is often replaced by rockers, sliders and push buttons. Switches are also available with only one stable state, which they return to when the toggle or push button is released.

Rotary *wafer* switches can have many poles and many *ways*. A way is similar to a throw but used when the number exceeds two. An SPDT switch could be called a single-pole, two-way switch, and a two-pole six-way switch would be able to connect either or both of two separate circuits to up to six others.

When using one of the more complicated switches for the first time, it is wise to use an ohmmeter to trace which contacts are joined when the switch is operated.

All switches have a maximum current rating which depends on the voltage used; if the rating is exceeded, the life of the switch will be shortened.

5.2 Voltage switching

Switches are designed to control currents, but they can be combined with a resistor to form a potential divider which provides a voltage input. In Figure 5.2(a), with the switch at the bottom, the output will be V_{CC} with the switch open and zero with it closed. These voltages are reversed in Figure 5.2(b). The switch could be a push action or a toggle switch, or even a reed switch as described in Section 5.4. Figure 5.2(c) shows how an SPDT switch can be used to connect an output to V_{CC} or zero at will.

5.3 The electromagnetic relay

An *electromagnetic relay* is simply a mechanical switch operated by an *electromagnet*. A simple form of relay is shown in Figure 5.3. When a current is passed through the coil the soft iron core becomes a magnet and attracts the iron

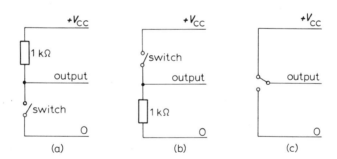

Figure 5.2 Voltage switching

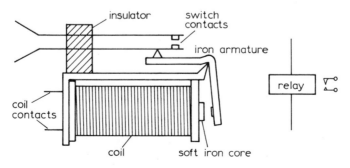

Figure 5.3 Relay with single-pole single-throw contacts

armature. The force of attraction increases as the armature gets nearer to the magnet and so, once the armature starts to move, it moves more and more rapidly under the action of a larger and larger force until it hits the magnet. This gives rise to a very fast switch. When the coil current is reduced the strength of the electromagnet becomes less, but it will not release the armature at once because the armature is close to it and therefore only a small current is required. The coil current has therefore to be reduced to well below its switch-on value for the relay to switch off. This overlap between switch on and switch off is called *hysteresis* and is a useful property of the relay.

The relay coil is electrically insulated from the switch contacts and so a relay is able to switch on or switch off circuits operating on different voltages from the coil operating voltage. The switch part of the relay may have several poles and use changeover contacts, and it can control several circuits at once.

Although the important electrical quantity in a relay is current, a particular relay is usually described by the voltage that must be applied across its coil for it to operate. The voltage given is for switch on.

5.4   The reed switch and reed relay

Although an ordinary relay gives a fast switch, it is not fast enough for some relay applications. Telephone exchanges are places where fast switching is required, and *reed relays* were de-

veloped for use in them. A *reed switch* consists of two thin strips of steel inside a glass tube (Figure 5.4). The strips are arranged so that their ends overlap but are a small distance apart. The switch is now open. If a magnetic field is brought near and parallel to the reed the two strips become magnets and are attracted to each other, so completing the circuit. The magnetic field can be provided by a permanent magnet or by a Solenoid, when the reed switch becomes a reed relay.

The main advantages of the reed relay are its fast switch and small size. In addition, the enclosure of the contacts in a glass tube enables them to be operated in an atmosphere of nitrogen, so that there is no sparking and the contacts last for a very long time.

5.5   The current-controlled transistor switch

In a transistor switch circuit the transistor takes the place of the movable contact in the mechanical switch. This means that the transistor must be either fully on or fully off, but never in a state somewhere in between.

The equation for the common-emitter current gain h_{FE} was introduced in Chapter 3:

$$h_{FE} = \frac{I_C}{I_B} \qquad \text{or} \qquad I_C = h_{FE}I_B$$

Consider the circuit of Figure 5.5. When the mechanical switch S is open there can be no base current I_B and so no collector current I_C. The transistor is off and the lamp will not light.

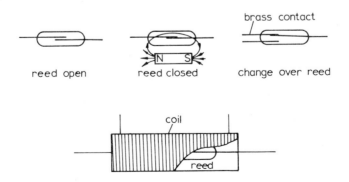

reed open   reed closed   change over reed

Figure 5.4   Reed relay

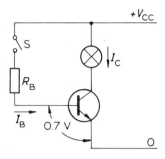

Figure 5.5

$$I_{C\,MAX} = \frac{V_{CC}}{R_C} = \frac{6}{100} = 0.06 \text{ A} \qquad \text{or} \quad 60 \text{ mA.}$$

We now calculate the least value for I_B that could give a 60 mA collector current:

$$I_B = \frac{I_C}{h_{FE}} = \frac{60}{200} = 0.3 \text{ mA}$$

To provide this base current the base resistor is given by

$$R_B = \frac{6 - 0.7}{0.3} = 18 \text{ k}\Omega$$

This resistor value would just switch on the lamp. It would be wise to make the base resistor less than this, say 10 kΩ, to make sure that the transistor is fully saturated.

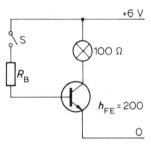

Figure 5.6

When the mechanical switch is closed a base current given by

$$I_B = \frac{V_{CC} - 0.7}{R_B}$$

flows into the base of the transistor. The 0.7 appears in the equation because the base/emitter junction of the transistor acts like a diode and, if the transistor is made of silicon, will drop 0.7 volts across it when it conducts.

Two factors now determine the collector current.

- The value of the base current just calculated.

- The value of the collector resistor R_C, which in this case is the lamp.

R_C puts a maximum value on to I_C such that

$$I_{C\,MAX} = \frac{V_{CC}}{R_C}$$

This will occur only if the transistor is fully on, and this state is achieved only if the value for I_C given by $I_C = h_{FE}I_B$ is equal to or greater than $I_{C\,MAX}$. The lamp will now be on. Once again an example will make this clear.

Example   *In the circuit of Figure 5.6 the supply voltage V_{CC} is 6 V, the lamp has a resistance of 100 Ω and the transistor a common-emitter current gain of 200. What is a suitable value for R_B?*

We need to make sure that when S is closed the transistor is fully switched on: that is, the current through the transistor and lamp is limited only by the resistance of the lamp. The transistor is then said to be *saturated*, and all the supply voltage will be dropped across the lamp and none across the transistor.

You may think that this is not a very useful circuit, and you would be right. The switch S could have switched on the lamp directly. Suppose, however, we replaced the switch and resistor R_B by an LDR (Figure 5.7). When the

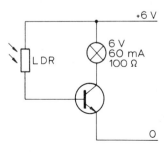

Figure 5.7

light intensity is low the LDR will have a high resistance and the base current will be very small – probably too small to even make the lamp glow. When the light intensity is high the resistance of the LDR will be low, and if the light is bright enough the base current might be large enough to saturate the transistor and so turn on the lamp with maximum brightness.

The circuit can now be considered as a complete system. It has an input transducer (the LDR), an output transducer (the lamp), and in between some electronic processing carried out by the transistor.

5.6   The voltage-controlled switch

The current-controlled switch of the previous section suffers from a number of defects. If the light intensity increases gradually a value will be reached when the lamp is partly illuminated. This is not what we want in a switch circuit, where the lamp should be either on or off. The value of the light intensity at which the light comes on is dependent on the h_{FE} of the transistor used, and this cannot be accurately predicted.

Our first basic circuit, the inverter, which was introduced in Chapter 3, can be considered as a switch that is controlled by the voltage at its input. As long as the voltage at the input is less than 0.7 V (V_{BE} for a silicon transistor) there can be no base current and the transistor must be switched off. The transistor will not switch on until the voltage is above 0.7 V, when the exact voltage needed to saturate the transistor depends on the h_{FE} of the transistor, the value of the base resistor and the collector current required.

Taking typical values of 200 for h_{FE} and 10 kΩ for R_B, and assuming that I_C is 9 mA, then the actual input voltage can be calculated. The base current I_B is given by

$$\frac{9}{200} = 0.045 \text{ mA}$$

and
$$I_B = \frac{V_{IN} - 0.7}{R_B}$$

$$0.045 = \frac{V_{IN} - 0.7}{10}$$

$$V_{IN} = 1.15 \text{ V}$$

In this case the transistor will be cut off when the input voltage is below 0.7 V and saturated when it is above 1.15 V. There is only the narrow band of 0.45 V when it is possible for the transistor to be partly conducting.

The actual voltages will vary in different circuits, but it is clear that a switch based on the inverter will be closer in action to a mechanical switch and less dependent on the h_{FE} of the transistor used.

To make the resistance change in a transducer operate the inverter we need a circuit that will convert the change in resistance to a change in voltage. The circuit required is the potential divider from Chapter 4. Any of the basic circuit potential dividers illustrated at the end of Chapter 4 could be combined with the inverter for light-controlled, heat-controlled and time delay switches. In the light and heat switches the variable resistors must be adjusted so that the output of the potential divider is 0.7 V at the light or heat level required for switching. In the time delay circuit the variable resistor is adjusted so that the capacitor takes the required time to reach 0.7 V.

Figure 5.8 shows two other potential divider basic circuits, this time containing switches.

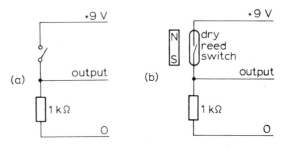

Figure 5.8   Potential divider circuits

5.7   Transducer driver circuits

Usually the output from the inverter has to operate an output transducer such as a relay or a lamp. The output of the inverter can only supply a few milliamperes without overloading, and transducers usually need much larger currents than this. The solution is to use another transistor to drive the transducer, and to design its circuit so that it only takes a small current from the inverter.

Two kinds of driver circuits are possible.

The common-emitter driver This is very similar to an inverter but with the transducer as the collector resistor (Figure 5.9). The base resistor must be large enough not to load the inverter. By the rule of ten it should be at least ten times the collector resistor of the inverter. In our case this gives a base resistor of 10 kΩ minimum. The transistor must be able to carry the current required by the transducer and have a high enough current gain h_{FE} to be able to conduct this current with a base resistor as high as 10 kΩ. The usual BC109 will not do. The TIS151 looks like an ordinary plastic-cased transistor, but inside it contains two transistors connected as a Darlington pair (Section 3.12). The result is a 'transistor' that has very high h_{FE} and can carry up to 1 A.

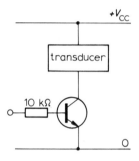

Figure 5.9 Common-emitter driver

The emitter-follower driver To understand this circuit (Figure 5.10) you must refer back to Section 3.11 and Figure 3.17. The collector of the transistor is connected directly to the positive supply rail, and the transducer is connected between the emitter and the zero line. No base resistor is required. The result is just as if the transducer was connected to the inverter directly but its resistance was increased by h_{FE}. The voltage supplied to the transducer when the inverter output is at V_{CC} is $V_{CC} - 0.7$ V.

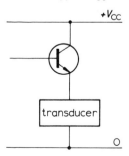

Figure 5.10 Emitter-follower driver

Once again the transistor needs to have high current-carrying capacity and gain, and the TIS151 is very suitable.

We now have all the ingredients necessary to make a complete system: an input circuit (the potential divider), a processing circuit (the inverter) and an output circuit (either driver circuit). Figures 5.11(a), (b) and (c) show some of the systems that can be made. Note that, in the circuits using a relay, a reverse-biased diode is connected in parallel with the coil. When a relay is switched off a voltage is generated across the coil in the opposite direction to the supply voltage. This voltge can be high enough to destroy the transistor, but the diode protects it by shorting out the voltage.

(a)

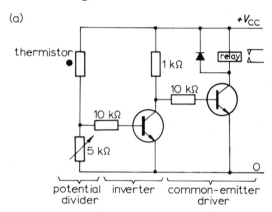

(b)

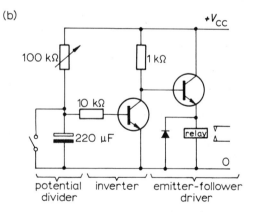

Figure 5.11(a) and (b)

You may need a circuit that performs the opposite function to the circuits given. For example, in the circuit of Figure 5.11(c) the lamp will be on when it is dark and go out if the LDR is illuminated. Suppose we wanted the light off when it is dark and to come on when light is falling on the LDR. One solution would be to use two identical inverters joined output to input as the processing circuit.

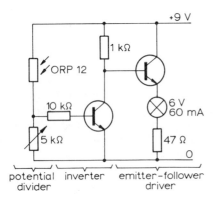

Figure 5.11(c)

5.8   The Schmitt trigger circuit

The voltage-controlled circuits of the previous section give a fast enough switch for many applications, but it is possible to find a transducer resistance for which the transistor is neither saturated nor cut off.

The *Schmitt trigger* circuit (Figure 5.12) uses *positive feedback* introduced through a shared emitter resistor to overcome this problem. You will see from Figure 5.12 that the circuit consists of two inverters in series sharing the emitter resistor R_E. The value of R_E decides the switching speed. A large R_E gives a fast switch but raises the lower output voltage. A good compromise is a

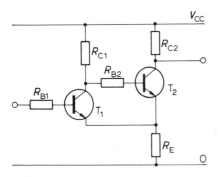

Figure 5.12   Schmitt trigger circuit

value of one-tenth of the collector resistor R_C.

A practical circuit is shown in Figure 5.13. The circuit will operate on a range of voltages, but if we assume a supply of 9 V the input and output voltages can be estimated.

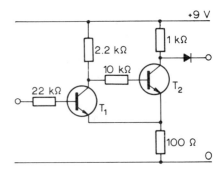

Figure 5.13   Practical Schmitt trigger circuit

Imagine the input voltage gradually increased from zero. At first transistor T_1 will be cut off and so the voltage at its collector will be V_{CC} (9 V in this case). This voltage is the input for the second transistor T_2, and so this will be saturated and there will be no voltage between its collector and emitter. The output can therefore be considered as the junction between two resistors R_C (1 kΩ) and R_E (100 Ω). The output voltage will therefore be

$$\frac{100 \times 9}{1000 + 100} = 0.8 \text{ V}$$

If the trigger circuit is to drive another circuit this may be a problem as it may be high enough to turn on the next transistor. If this problem arises it may be cured by connecting a forward-biased diode in the output lead.

The input voltage is still rising, and eventually it will reach just above the low output value calculated above plus 0.7 V. That is, in this case, 1.5 V. The exact switch-on voltage is best found by experiment. Above this input voltage T_1 will be saturated and T_2 will be cut off, giving an output voltage of V_{CC} or 9 V.

If the input voltage is now reduced the circuit will not switch back at the same voltage as it switched on but at a lower voltage. Imagine the input slowly falling from 9 V. T_1 is saturated, making its emitter voltage and collector voltage the same and equal to the junction of the potential divider made from the 2.2 kΩ and 100 Ω

resistors. This voltage is

$$\frac{100 \times 9}{2200 + 100} = 0.4 \text{ V}$$

The base of T_1 will be 0.7 V above this, giving a switch-off voltage of 1.1 V.

As mentioned in Section 5.3, this overlap between switch-on and switch-off voltages is called hysteresis. It is a useful property as it gives a stable switch, not affected by small variations in the resistance of the input transducer.

5.9 The operational amplifier as a switch circuit

Figure 5.14(a) shows an operational amplifier connected as a switch. Voltage V is set by the potential divider formed by R_1 and R_2. This is the switching voltage for the circuit. As long as the input voltage is lower than V the output will be at a voltage close to the negative rail. When the input voltage exceeds V the output will rapidly rise until it is close to the positive supply rail. Its action is therefore opposite to that of a transistor inverter. Like the inverter, though, there is a range of voltages on either side of V for which the output has a value between the two extremes. For a good switch this voltage range should be as small as possible. Given an opamp with an open-loop gain of 100 000 and a supply voltage of 9 V, this input range will be of width

$$\frac{9}{100\,000} = 0.00009 \text{ V}.$$

You can see that the circuit is a good switch.

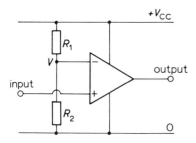

Figure 5.14(a) Operational amplifier as a switch

Figure 5.14(b) shows a basic circuit based on the opamp switch. It has the advantage over the previous circuit that the reference voltage can be varied using a potentiometer wired as a potential divider.

Another form of the comparator, in which the output goes down to the zero rail when the input is above the reference value set by the potentiometer, is shown in Figure 5.14(c).

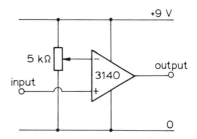

Figure 5.14(b) Basic circuit based on opamp switch

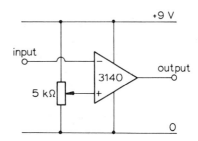

Figure 5.14(c) Another form of comparator

Example *Design an engine temperature warning light circuit to warn the driver if a car's radiator is about to boil.*

The input transducer will be a thermistor, and this will form part of an input potential divider. The other resistor in the potential divider can be a variable so that the voltage at which switching takes place can be adjusted, but we will need some information about the thermistor before we can choose a suitable potentiometer.

Type GM47 is a miniature bead thermistor made for temperature measurement. Its resistance/temperature characteristic is shown in Figure 5.15. If we want the circuit to switch at 100 °C we need to know the resistance at this temperature. From the graph this is 5 kΩ. If a 10 kΩ potentiometer is connected as a variable resistor and adjusted to 5 kΩ the output voltage from the potential divider will be $\frac{1}{2} V_{CC}$ at 100 °C. The thermistor should be the upper half of the potential divider so that the input voltage will be below $\frac{1}{2} V_{CC}$ when the thermistor is cold.

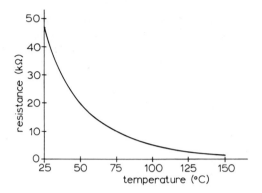

Figure 5.15 Resistance/temperature characteristic of GM47 miniature bead thermistor

The opamp trigger circuit must now be designed to switch at $\frac{1}{2}V_{CC}$, and this is easily arranged by making $R_1 = R_2 = 10\text{ k}\Omega$. There remains only a warning lamp to go on to the dashboard. We could use the usual lamp and driver circuit, but most cars now use light-emitting diodes; an LED can be driven directly from the output of the opamp.

Figure 5.16 shows the complete system. Note the current-limiting resistor in series with the LED, calculated as described in Section 3.8:

$$R = \frac{10 - 2}{10} = 0.8\text{ k}\Omega = 800\ \Omega \quad (820\ \Omega)$$

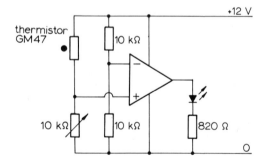

Figure 5.16

You may wonder why the voltage used in this calculation is 10 V rather than the actual supply voltage of 12 V. This is because it was assumed that the opamp used was a 741, and the output of this opamp cannot get closer to the supply rails than 2 V. This means that when the non-inverting input is low the output is not at 0 V

but at 2 V, and when the input is high the output rises to 10 V instead of 12 V.

This puts some limitations on the supply voltages that can be used. Obviously with a supply voltage of 4 V the output could not move, and even 6 V would only allow a swing from 2 to 4 V. A problem also arises if the output of the opamp is used to drive another circuit such as an inverter. Even when the output is low it is above the 0.7 V needed to make the transistor turn on. Three silicon diodes connected in series with the output so that they are forward biased will drop 2.1 V and so solve the problem. They are not required when driving an LED as this already drops 2 V across it. When using the circuit to drive a lamp or relay through an emitter follower, use a supply voltage 4 V higher than the voltage needed by the lamp or relay to allow for the 2 V lost across the diodes plus the 2 V the output falls short of the supply. Therefore for a 6 V lamp use a 10 V supply.

The 741 was designed some time ago. Some of the more recent opamps have outputs that go right down to the negative supply rail and so no output diodes are needed. An example of this is the CA3140E which has the same arrangement of pins as a 741. This opamp also has a very high input resistance, which is an additional advantage, but it costs rather more.

The kind of supply used in all the circuits described in this chapter consists of two rails, one positive and one zero. In most published opamp circuits a dual supply is used in which there are three rails. One is $+V_{CC}$, one is $-V_{CC}$ and the other is zero. A dual supply requires two batteries or a special mains power supply. See Figure 3.21.

A dual-supply version of the temperature switch is shown in Figure 5.17.

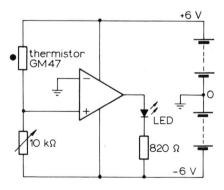

Figure 5.17 Dual-supply version of temperature switch

5.10 The opamp Schmitt trigger

Circuits of the Schmitt trigger type have the ideal switch characteristic. They can move their outputs from low to high or the reverse very quickly, and they have the useful property of hysteresis.

An inverting comparator can be converted to a Schmitt by the addition of positive feedback. Figure 5.18(a) shows an inverting comparator with a reference voltage set at $\frac{1}{2}V_{CC}$ by two $10\,k\Omega$ resistors. When the input is below $\frac{1}{2}V_{CC}$ the output will be near to V_{CC}, and when the input is above the reference voltage the output will be close to zero.

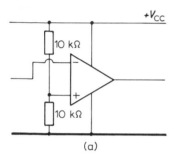

(a)

Figure 5.18(a)

Compare this circuit with the inverting Schmitt of Figure 5.18(b). One extra resistor has been added which joins the output to the non-inverting input, i.e. positive feedback. This resistor has been made equal to the resistors providing the reference voltage, as this makes the following arithmetic easier.

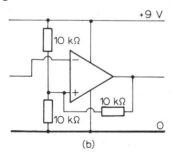

(b)

Figure 5.18(b)

Imagine that the input voltage is low. The output voltage will be at $+V_{CC}$ and the feedback resistor and the upper reference resistor will be in parallel. The combination of two $10\,k\Omega$ resistances in parallel is $5\,k\Omega$, and a potential divider made up of a $5\,k\Omega$ upper resistor and a $10\,k\Omega$

lower resistor has a voltage of 6 V at its junction if the supply is 9 V. This 6 V forms the circuit's reference voltage and the output will not switch to low unless the input rises above 6 V. Suppose this has just happened. The output is zero and the feedback resistor is now in parallel with the lower reference resistor, giving a voltage at the junction of 3 V. At the point of switching the input is rising and the reference voltage is falling, giving a fast switch. If the input is now reduced it will have to go below 3 V before the circuit switches back, an overlap of 3 V.

You will see that the lower the feedback resistor the more feedback there is, the faster the switch, and the more the hysteresis. Designers are usually content with less feedback than we have used in our example. A larger-feedback resistor is used in the opamp version of the light switch of Figure 5.11(c) (Figure 5.19).

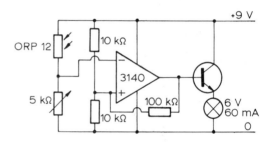

Figure 5.19 Opamp version of light switch

5.11 The opamp ramp generator

This basic circuit is an alternative to the capacitor/resistor time delay circuit of Chapter 4. This circuit has the advantage that the voltage changes linearly with time (it changes by equal amounts in equal times) and so it is easy to forecast the length of the delay. The circuit is shown in Figure 5.20.

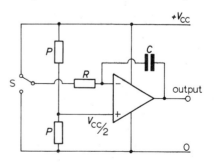

Figure 5.20 Opamp ramp generator

As long as switch S is connecting the input to V_{CC}, current will flow through the input resistor R and into the capacitor. The capacitor charges, making the voltage at the output fall at a rate given by:

$$\text{rate of change of voltage} = \frac{\text{input voltage}}{RC}$$

The input voltage in the equation is measured relative to the non-inverting input, which is held at $\frac{1}{2}V_{CC}$ by the two equal resistors P, i.e. input voltage $= \frac{1}{2}V_{CC}$. If switch S is changed so that the input is connected to earth, the output will ramp up at the same rate.

Figure 5.21(a) shows a practical form of the ramp generator, a basic circuit. If you compare the practical circuit with the theoretical circuit of Figure 5.20 you will notice a number of modifications. Input resistor R consists of a 1 MΩ variable and a 10 kΩ fixed resistor in series giving, with the 1 μF capacitor, an output voltage which

changes at a maximum rate of 450 V/s and a minimum rate of 4.5 V/s when the input is connected to earth. Use the equation to check these figures.

The reference voltage at the non-inverting input can be varied between 3 and 6 V. It was assumed to be set to 4.5 V in the calculation above. A push switch allows the output to be reset to zero when required. The capacitor is short-circuited by a high resistor. The function of this resistor is described at the end of Section 5.16.

Figure 5.21(b) shows how a ramp generator could be used to produce a timer circuit which lights an LED after a preset time interval. The input voltage at point A is set so that it is a fraction of a volt lower than the reference voltage set at point B. The output of the ramp generator will now ramp up very slowly when switch S is released so that delays of up to 100 s can be obtained. The difference between the two voltages at A and B is the input voltage and if this is very small then, by the equation, the rate of change of voltage will be small.

5.12   The bistable multivibrator

Consider two transistor inverters connected input to output as shown in Figure 5.22. Suppose that transistor T_1 is switched off so that its collector voltage is V_{CC}, i.e. the voltage at output 1 is V_{CC}. Current will flow into T_2 so that it is turned on, and the voltage at output 2 is zero. This output holds the base of T_1 low and so makes sure that it remains turned off. The circuit is in a stable state and will remain like this unless

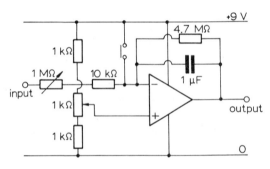

Figure 5.21(a)   Practical form of ramp generator

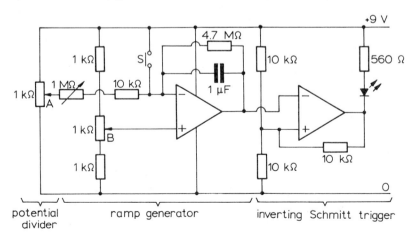

Figure 5.21(b)   Ramp generator timer circuit

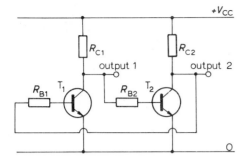

Figure 5.22 Bistable circuit

the power is switched off. Try assuming that T_1 is turned on, and you will find that there is another stable state with output 1 at zero and output 2 at V_{CC}. The two stable states give the circuit its names of *bistable* or *flip-flop*.

This circuit will not be very useful unless we can change it from one state to the other, and this can be achieved by adding two more resistors to the transistor bases. The result is a *set/reset* (SR) bistable which is shown in a practical form in Figure 5.23. This new basic circuit has outputs Q

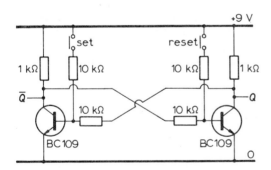

Figure 5.23 Set-reset bistable

and $\overline{Q}$ which are always opposite to each other as explained above, and which depend not only on the voltages applied to the set and reset inputs but also on the past history of the circuit. For the first time we have a circuit that can remember a previous state. A circuit of this type is called a *latch*.

The properties of the circuit are best described by a table (Figure 5.24) where a 'high' voltage is one of more than $\frac{1}{2}V_{CC}$ and a 'low' voltage is one of less than 0.7 V.

Set input voltage	Reset input voltage	Q output voltage	$\overline{Q}$ output voltage
high	high	low	low
high	low	high	low
low	high	low	high
low	low	both outputs remain as they were when the last input went low		

Figure 5.24 Bistable latch output states

Figure 5.25 shows a simple burglar alarm using reed switches. The switches are let into the frames of the windows and doors so that when all are closed the switches are operated by magnets. If any window or door is opened the magnet moves away from the switch and the alarm sounds. A latch is needed so that the burglar cannot switch off the alarm by closing the window behind him. Closing the reset switch will hold the Q output at zero whether the windows and doors are open or closed, allowing them to be used normally. Returning the reset switch to open activates the alarm ready for the next burglar.

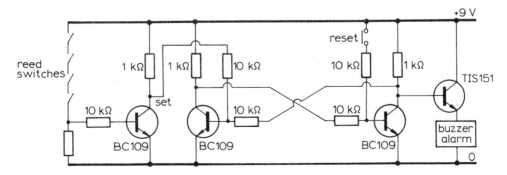

Figure 5.25 Burglar alarm using reed switches

5.13 The monostable multivibrator

Compare the circuit of Figure 5.26 with that of the bistable (Figure 5.23). The left-hand half of the two circuits is identical, and both use positive feedback from the Q output into this half. The monostable, however, uses a combination of a capacitor and a resistor to join the two stages.

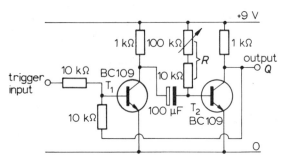

Figure 5.26   Monostable circuit

With the trigger input held low, T_1 will be off and so its collector voltage will be 9 V. T_2 will be turned on by the current flowing into its base through resistor R, and so its base voltage will be 0.7 V and its collector voltage, output Q, zero.

Suppose the trigger voltage is now raised high enough to turn on T_1. As T_1 turns on its collector voltage will fall to zero, taking the left-hand plate of the capacitor down with it. The capacitor originally had $9 - 0.7 = 8.3$ V across it. This cannot change suddenly, and so the base of T_2 will be taken down to 8.3 V *below* zero. This turns T_2 off, and it will not turn on again until the capacitor has charged through resistor R sufficiently for the base of T_2 to reach 0.7 V again. This takes a time of $0.7\,RC$ seconds, where R is in ohms and C in farads (or, more usefully, R is in megohms and C in microfarads).

All the time that T_2 is off the Q output will be at 9 V. The feedback loop gives a fast switch and holds T_1 on during the time the output is high even if the original trigger voltage is removed.

The total function of the circuit is therefore to produce a positive voltage pulse lasting for $0.7\,RC$ seconds at the beginning of a positive trigger pulse. The length of the trigger pulse is not important and any trigger pulses which occur during the output pulse are ignored. The circuit can therefore be added to our collection of timing circuits.

Using the values given in the basic circuit of Figure 5.26, the length of the positive output pulse would have a maximum value of $0.7 \times 110 \times 0.1 = 7.7$ s. The minimum value will be 0.7 s.

Figure 5.27 shows the circuit for a transistorized door bell. The bell rings for the same length of time however long the switch is pushed.

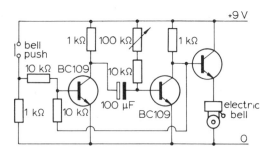

Figure 5.27   Transistorized door bell

5.14 The astable multivibrator

The bistable has two stable states. The monostable has only one, which it returns to after completing its output pulse. The astable has no stable states at all but constantly switches from one state to the other. This is achieved by combining two timing circuits of the type used as the output half of the monostable. As soon as one half has completed its output pulse it triggers the other so that an output pulse is obtained from Q and $\overline{Q}$ in turn.

The circuit diagram is shown in Figure 5.28(a) and (b). Check for yourself that the two circuits are identical.

The time that the Q output is high is called the *mark* and the time it is zero is the *space*. The ratio of high to low is known as the *mark-to-space ratio*. The outputs from Q and $\overline{Q}$ are shown in Figure 5.28(c) and are of a form known as a *square wave*.

Resistors R_1 and R_2 and capacitors C_1 and C_2 are often made equal to each other when the mark-to-space ratio becomes one to one and the total time for one complete cycle is $1.4\,RC$. The astable is now producing a square wave of frequency given by

$$\text{frequency} = \frac{1}{1.4\,RC}\ \text{Hz}$$

You will see from the equation that the frequency of an astable can be varied by altering either the capacitor value or the resistor value.

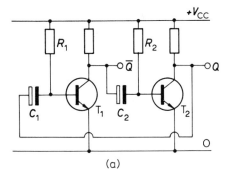

(a)

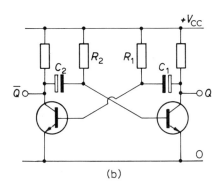

(b)

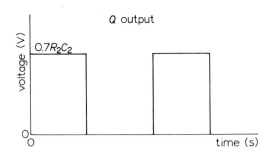

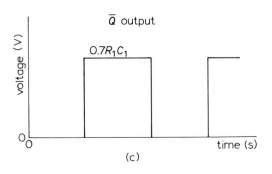

(c)

Figure 5.28 Astable multivibrator. (*a*) and (*b*) Two versions of circuit (*c*) Output voltages

Figure 5.29 (on the next page) shows some practical astable circuits. Circuit (a) shows the most simple way of varying the frequency, but with the disadvantage that the mark-to-space ratio also alters. Circuit (b) shows a form of (a) suitable as the tone generator of a stylus-type electronic organ. The 100 kΩ presets are individually adjusted to give the notes of the musical scale. Circuit (c) shows how frequency can be varied and the mark-to-space ratio held constant at one to one. The dotted line shows that the two potentiometers are *ganged*; that is, both are operated by the same spindle. Ganged potentiometers are expensive, and so (d) shows how the same result can be achieved by just varying an input voltage, a *voltage-controlled oscillator* (VCO). Circuit (d) is useful enough to be added to our list of basic circuits.

All the astables so far have frequencies in the audio range, but it is possible to have very low frequencies by the use of electrolytic capacitors. Figure 5.29(e) is a lamp flasher, and you can see from it that the positive plate of the capacitor has to go to the transistor's collector. The frequency of the flasher could be varied by any of the methods described above.

5.15 The opamp astable and monostable

There is an opamp version of most transistor circuits, and the astable is no exception. The circuit shown in Figure 5.30(a) is based on the inverting Schmitt trigger of Section 5.10 (Figure 5.18(b)).

You will remember that this circuit had a switch-on voltage of 6 V when the input was rising and a switch off voltage of 3 V when the input voltage was falling. Three components have been added, a capacitor and a series resistor made up of a fixed 1 kΩ and a variable 1 MΩ. We will call the combined resistance R (Figure 5.30(b)).

Imagine the capacitor charged to a voltage below 6 V. The circuit will be switched off and the output will be high. The capacitor can therefore continue to charge towards V_{CC} through R. When the voltage across the capacitor exceeds 6 V the Schmitt will trigger and its output will fall to zero, taking the end of R with it. The capacitor will now start to discharge through R towards zero, but before it reaches zero the voltage at the input of the Schmitt will be taken below 3 V, the output will go high once more and the cycle will begin

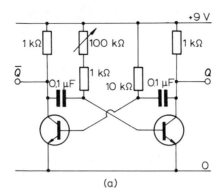

(a)

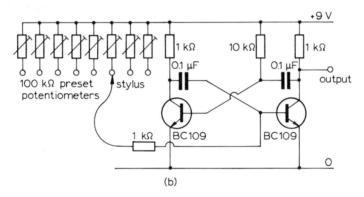

(b)

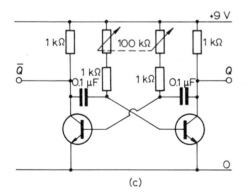

(c)

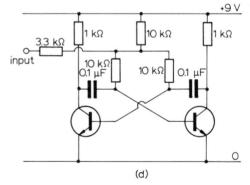

(d)

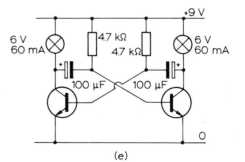

(e)

Figure 5.29   Practical astable circuits
(*a*)   Simple way of varying frequency
(*b*)   Tone generator
(*c*)   Variation of frequency with constant mark-to-space ratio
(*d*)   Voltage-controlled oscillator
(*e*)   Lamp flasher

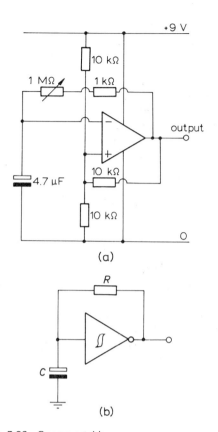

(a)

(b)

Figure 5.30 Opamp astable

possible – near the zero rail in one case, and the negative rail in the other. If switch S is now closed the output will suddenly rise to the positive rail voltage. The capacitor will be unable to charge instantly so that the non-inverting input will be forced to rise as well, taking it above the original voltage of the inverting input. The output will now stay high while the capacitor charges through the potentiometer until the non-inverting voltage falls below the inverting voltage, when the circuit will revert to its original state. The circuit could be triggered by connecting S or another switch circuit directly to the inverting input, but this would have the disadvantage that if S was left closed the output would remain high for ever. With the circuit shown the 0.047 μF capacitor transfers the trigger pulse and the 15 kΩ resistor allows the capacitor to discharge.

The period of the output pulse is about RC where R is 1 MΩ maximum and C is 100 μF in (a). The period can therefore be up to 100 s. It will be shorter in (b) because this timing capacitor will have to be non-electrolytic.

again. The capacitor is constantly charging from 3 to 6 V and discharging from 6 to 3 V. While charging the output is high and while discharging it is low. The output is therefore a square wave of one-to-one mark-to-space ratio.

The frequency depends on the exact switching voltages, but is approximately given by

$$f = \frac{1}{RC}$$

where C is in farads and R in ohms, or C is in microfarads and R in megohms.

The above theory can be applied to any inverting Schmitt trigger, and various astables based on IC Schmitts can be made.

Single-ended and dual-power-supply versions of a monostable are shown in Figure 5.31(a) and (b). In either version the inverting input is biased a few volts positive and the non-inverting input is held at zero by a 1 MΩ potentiometer. The inverting input is therefore higher than the non-inverting and the output will be as low as

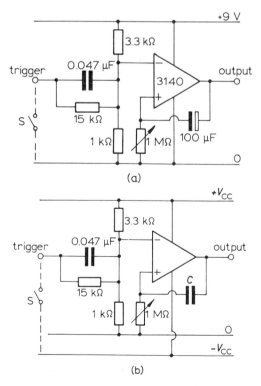

(a)

(b)

Figure 5.31 Opamp monostables (*a*) Single-ended version (*b*) Dual-power-supply version

5.16   The 555 timer IC

Astables and monostables are so useful that someone was sure to invent an IC specifically to make them. The 555 is such a chip. Its pin arrangement is shown in Figure 5.32(a) and its internal arrangement in Figure 5.32(b). There is no need, of course, to understand how an IC works to be able to use it. However, this particular one is a good example of a system made up out of the various circuits that we have studied, and is included for those who like to know why as well as how.

The 555 is shown connected as an astable. The components inside the dotted line are part of the IC.

When the circuit is first switched on the capacitor is discharged and the voltages at both comparator inputs are zero. The output of comparator A is low and the output of comparator B is high. The high from B sets the bistable so that Q and the output are V_{CC} and $\bar{Q}$ is zero. The transistor is turned off. The capacitor charges through P and Q and the voltage at 2 and 6 rises. When it is above $(1/3)V_{CC}$, comparator B changes its output, to zero but this does not affect the bistable which is set and reset by high voltages. When the capacitor reaches $(2/3)V_{CC}$, comparator A changes its output from zero to V_{CC} and the bistable is reset, making the output go low and $\bar{Q}$ high. The high value of $\bar{Q}$ turns the transistor on, which short-circuits the junction of P and Q to ground (gnd). The capacitor will now start to discharge through Q alone until the voltage at 2 is below $(1/3)V_{CC}$, when the bistable is set, the output rises and the capacitor starts to charge once more.

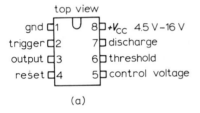

top view

gnd ⊏1   8⊐ +V_{CC} 4.5 V – 16 V
trigger ⊏2   7⊐ discharge
output ⊏3   6⊐ threshold
reset ⊏4   5⊐ control voltage

(a)

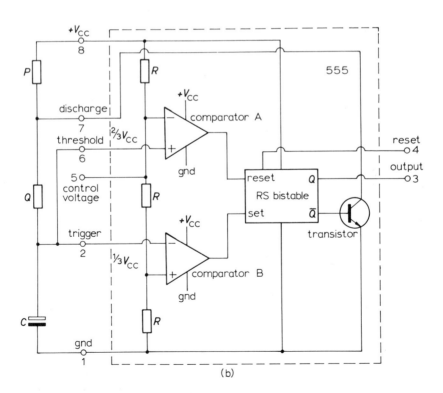

(b)

Figure 5.32   555 timer integrated circuit (*a*) Pin arrangement (*b*) Internal circuit

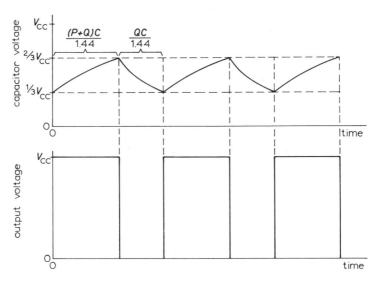

Figure 5.33 Relationship between capacitor voltage and output voltage for 555 timer connected as stable

After the first time the capacitor spends part of its time charging through P and Q in series from $(1/3)V_{CC}$ to $(2/3)V_{CC}$ and the rest of its time discharging from $(2/3)V_{CC}$ to $(1/3)V_{CC}$ through resistor Q. While charging is taking place the output is high, and it is low during the capacitor's discharge period. The output is a square wave with the mark longer than the space. Figure 5.33 shows the relationship in phase between the voltage across the capacitor and the output voltage. The frequency can be calculated from

$$f = \frac{1.44}{(P + 2Q)C} \text{ Hz}$$

If Q is made much larger than P, the mark-to-space ratio becomes nearly one to one and the frequency equation reduces to

$$f = \frac{0.72}{QC} \text{ Hz}$$

The 555 will produce a good square wave over a wide range of frequencies. P and Q can have values between $1 \text{ k}\Omega$ and $1 \text{ M}\Omega$, C can vary between a few nanofarads and $1000 \, \mu\text{F}$, and the supply voltage range is from 3 V to 15 V.

The output can supply currents up to 200 mA. It is best to protect the output by a current-limiting resistor if there is a possibility that it might be short-circuited to earth. Figure 5.34

shows a practical astable circuit. Note that Q has been made variable. When a fixed-frequency astable is required it is usual to connect the control input to ground by a 10 nF capacitor. In the circuit shown there is a voltage input to the control input via a $10 \text{ k}\Omega$ resistor. This converts the astable into a voltage-controlled oscillator (VCO). A high voltage at the input tends to raise the voltages at the junctions of the internal potential divider to above $(1/3)V_{CC}$ and $(2/3)V_{CC}$. The upper voltage will rise more than the lower, so increasing the voltage range that the capacitor charges and discharges through. The charge and discharge periods will therefore be increased and

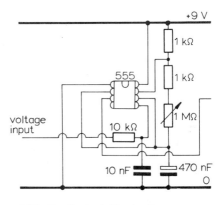

Figure 5.34 Practical astable circuit

the frequency reduced. In a similar way a low input voltage will reduce the internal voltage and narrow the gap between them so increasing the frequency.

As an alternative the input voltage can be applied to the reset input. If the voltage falls below 0.7 V on this pin the oscillation stops. Type 555 astables produce voltage spikes on the power rails which sometimes interfere with other circuits. If this is a problem, connect a 100 μF capacitor as a *decoupling capacitor* between the power rails.

The 555 can also be used as a monostable, and the circuit arrangement for this is shown in Figure 5.35. In its normal state the trigger input is held at V_{CC} by the 10 kΩ resistor. The bistable is in its reset state with its Q output low and its $\overline{Q}$ output high. $\overline{Q}$ holds the transistor on, which prevents the capacitor from beginning to charge. A push-on switch S reduces the trigger voltage to below (1/3)V_{CC}, the output of comparator B goes high and the bistable is set. The output is now high and $\overline{Q}$ low, so turning the transistor off. The capacitor is now free to charge through resistor P

and does so until the voltage at pin 6, the threshold, exceeds (2/3)V_{CC}. The bistable is now reset by comparator A, the output drops and $\overline{Q}$ rises to turn on the transistor. The transistor short-circuits the capacitor to ground and restores the circuit to its resting state.

The result of all this is that a square pulse is produced lasting for the time taken for the capacitor to charge through P from zero to (2/3)V_{CC} each time the switch is pushed.

What would happen if the switch was held down? The answer is that the output pulse would last until it was released. The practical circuit of Figure 5.36 shows a way in which this difficulty can be overcome. Each time the input is connected to ground, either by a switch or a previous circuit, the same length of output pulse will be produced however long the input is held low (Figure 5.37). The time delay produced by a 555 monostable can be calculated from

$$T = 1.1 \, PC$$

In the practical circuit P is the sum of the 1 kΩ and 1 MΩ potentiometers.

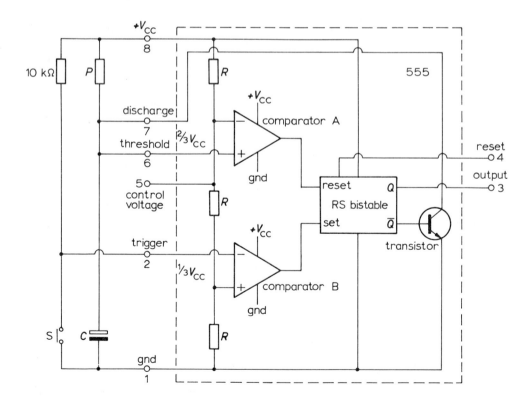

Figure 5.35   Monostable circuit based on 555 integrated circuit

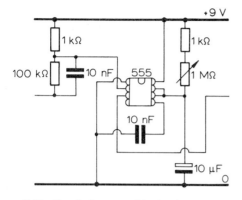

Figure 5.36 Practical monostable circuit

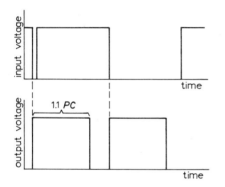

Figure 5.37 Input and output voltages for practical monostable circuit

The 555 voltage-to-frequency converter can now be combined with the ramp generator of Section 5.11, the opamp astable of Section 5.15, some kind of driver circuit, and an 80 Ω loudspeaker to produce some interesting and offensive noises. The circuit is shown in Figure 5.38.

The astable is adjusted to produce a slow square wave and the ramp generator converts this to a triangle wave. As the ramp generator output ramps up and down the frequency produced by the 555 rises and falls, giving a siren-like effect. There are some problems, however. The ramp generator would like an input which varied by the same amount above and below its reference voltage. Failing this, the output will gradually move towards one of the power rails and finally rest there permanently. The 4.7 MΩ resistor tends to prevent this, but for a particular input the reference voltage must be adjusted until it is approximately correct. The best way of doing this is to connect a meter between the ramp generator output and the zero line and adjust the 1 kΩ potentiometer until the output is, on average, mid-way between 0 and V_{CC}. The rate of change of the output voltage must also be adjusted by using the 1 MΩ potentiometer. Too slow a ramp (resistance too large) will give a triangle wave of very small amplitude and so little variation in the sound. Too fast a ramp (resistance too low) will allow the triangle to hit the power rails and give a sound more like a police car than a siren. If a two-tone sound is all you want it can be achieved by connecting the astable directly to the 555 input. No ramp generator is needed.

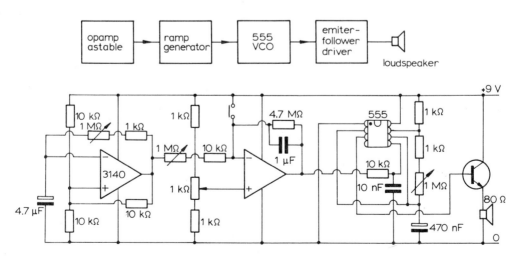

Figure 5.38 A circuit to produce 'interesting' noises

5.17   The opamp buffer circuit

Using an opamp it is possible to produce a circuit which copies a voltage from input to output but allows the voltage to deliver more current. The technical way to describe this action is to say that it has a high input resistance and a low output resistance.

The emitter-follower driver circuit of Sections 3.11 and 5.7 is a circuit of this type, but it has the disadvantage of making the output always 0.7 V lower than the input.

The voltage gain of the opamp is reduced to one by 100% DC negative feedback caused by joining output to inverting input. The input resistance into the non-inverting input is very high. In fact it is often too high, and in the basic circuit of Figure 5.39 two 220 kΩ resistors reduce the input resistance to 100 kΩ.

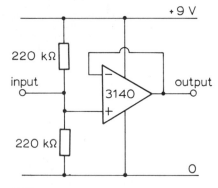

Figure 5.39

Summary

Switches

Mechanical switches are described by the number of separate switches operated by the same control – the number of poles – and the number of connections that each pole can make – the ways.

Relays

Electromechanical switch. Gives the advantages of a fairly fast switch with hysteresis. Input circuit insulated from output circuit.

Basic circuits

Switch unit

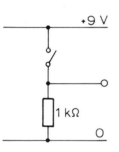

Voltage rises from zero to the supply voltage when the switch is closed.

Magnetic unit

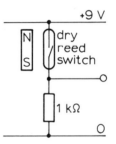

Voltage rises from zero to the supply voltage when the switch is closed.

Comparator

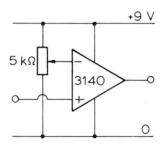

If the input is below the reference voltage set by the potentiometer the output is zero. If the input is above the reference voltage the output is high.

Inverting comparator

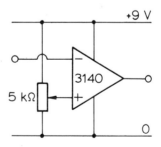

If the input is below the reference voltage set by the potentiometer the output is high. If the input is above the reference voltage the output is zero.

Ramp generator

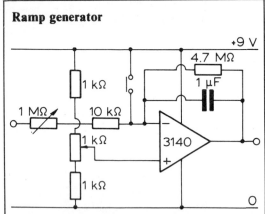

The output voltage ramps towards V_{CC} when the push switch is released at a rate determined by the potentiometer and the input voltage.

Opamp monostable

The output goes high for a period set by the potentiometer, when the input is suddenly taken low.

Common-emitter driver

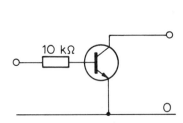

The output transducer should be connected between the output and V_{CC}.

Opamp buffer

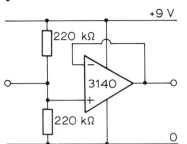

Buffer to join circuits where the rule of ten is not obeyed.

Relay unit

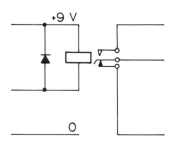

The relay must be chosen to suit the value of V_{CC} and driven by the common-emitter driver.

Inverting Schmitt

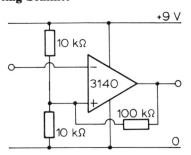

If the input is below V_{CC}/the output is high. If the input is below V_{CC}/the output is low. Exhibits hysteresis.

Bistable latch

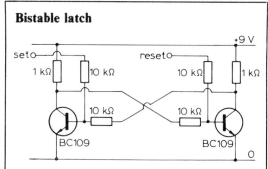

The output goes high if a high voltage is applied to the set input and remains high until reset by the switch.

Transistor monostable

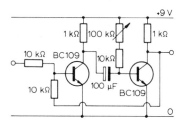

The output goes high if a high voltage is applied to the trigger input and remains high for a time determined by the potentiometer. Maximum 7 s.

Transistor astable/VCO

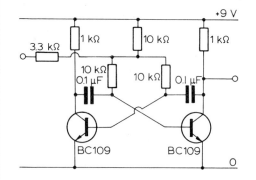

Square-wave output of audio frequency, varied by input voltage.

555 astable/VCO

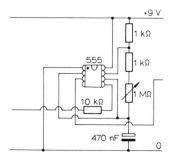

Square-wave output of frequency varied by input voltage. Range 1.5 Hz to 1.5 kHz. When fixed-frequency astable required connect control to ground with 10 nF capacitor.

Opamp astable

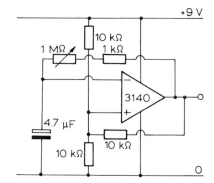

Square-wave output. 0.2 Hz to 200 Hz.

555 monostable

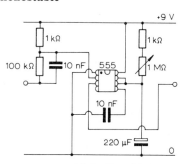

The output goes high if a high voltage is applied to the input, and remains high for a period of up to 10 s.

Lamp unit (EF)

+9 V

6 V
60 mA

47 Ω

O

Lamp unit to be driven by emitter-follower
driver. Omit resistor for voltages below 9 V.

LED indicator (CE)

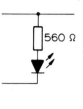

560 Ω

LED lights when input voltage is low. Can be
driven directly from opamp output or by
common-emitter driver.

LED indicator (EF)

560 Ω

LED lights when input voltage is high. Can be
driven directly from opamp output or by
emitter-follower driver.

Loudspeaker

80 Ω

The loudspeaker can be driven directly by a
driver or through a large coupling capacitor
from the opamp. Class B output stage.

Lamp unit (CE)

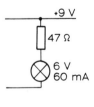

+9 V

47 Ω

6 V
60 mA

O

Lamp unit to be driven by common-emitter
driver. Omit resistor for voltages below 9 V.

Questions

1 Show how by the use of two SPDT switches it is possible to design a stair light system where the light can be turned on and off at the top or bottom of the stairs.

2 Study the following circuits, and for each one describe the action of the circuit and then answer the question below it.

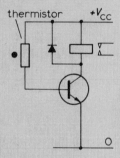

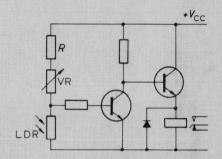

Why is the diode connected in parallel to the relay?

What is the function of the variable resistor?

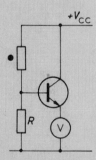

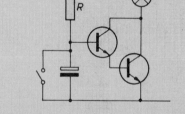

Is the transistor connected in common-emitter or emitter-follower mode?

What is this combination of transistors called, and what is its purpose?

3 Describe the qualities of a good transistor switch and use them to compare current-biased and voltage-biased switches.

4 The action of a relay has been compared with that of a Schmitt trigger circuit. In what ways are they similar, and in what ways do they differ?

5 Describe how the systems (a)–(f) shown would work, and suggest a possible use for each from the list (i)–(vi) provided.

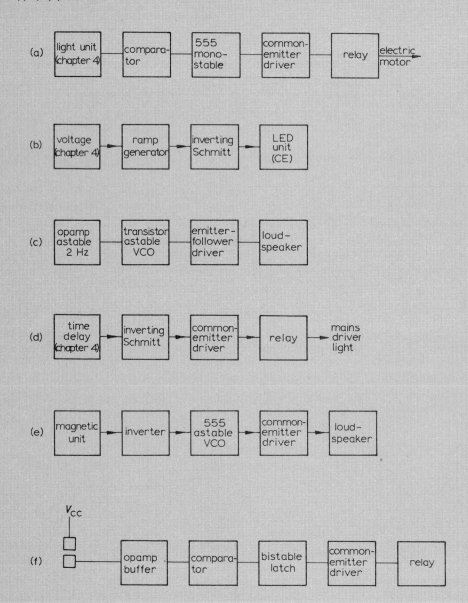

  (i) **Light switch delay:** allows you to reach the house before the garage light goes off.
 (ii) **Egg timer.**
(iii) **Magnet detector.**
 (iv) **Automatic garage door:** opens at a headlight flash.
  (v) **Two-tone alarm.**
 (vi) **Touch switch to turn on TV.**

6

Basic logic circuits

6.1 What are logic circuits?

Logic circuits were originally developed to process the data inside digital computers, but their use has since spread into all branches of electronics.

Inside a digital computer information is expressed as *binary numbers*, that is, numbers consisting of ones and zeros. These binary states are represented by low and high voltages. The information is transferred and processed inside the computer according to rules built into the computer in the form of circuits called *logic gates*. The term *gate* comes about because the circuits can stop information or allow it to pass, and the word *logic* because they do so according to rules that can be described by logical statements using the words AND, OR and NOT.

6.2 The AND gate

In ordinary language we can use the word AND in a conditional statement such as 'John will go to the cinema if he can borrow the car AND he can afford the ticket.' 'Going to the cinema' is conditional on 'borrowing the car' and 'affording the ticket'. Let us represent the first condition by its initial *B* and the second by *A*. Going to the cinema is represented by *Q*.

We can adopt the binary system and use *logical one* (1) for a satisfied condition and *logical zero* (0) for one unsatisfied. (1) and (0) can also show if the output condition is allowed or not. The original statement now becomes: 'Only if *A* is (1) AND *B* is (1) will output *Q* be (1).'

This statement could also represent all other statements of the same type, and can be conveniently summed up by a special kind of table called a *truth table*. Other ways in which the AND function can be described are the *logic symbol* and the *Venn diagram*.

All three representations are shown in Figure 6.1. Both the British and American symbols are shown. In the Venn diagram the shaded part shows the part that satisfies the AND condition.

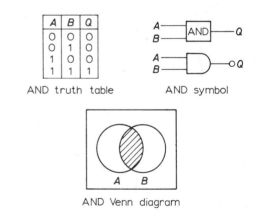

A	B	Q
O	O	O
O	1	O
1	O	O
1	1	1

AND truth table

AND symbol

AND Venn diagram

Figure 6.1 Representations of the AND gate

6.3 The OR gate

OR is another conditional word, e.g. 'John can go to the cinema if either his mother OR his father will give him the money.' If going to the cinema is again *Q*, mother giving money is *A* and father giving money is *B*, then we can produce a symbol, a truth table and a Venn diagram representing the OR function (Figure 6.2).

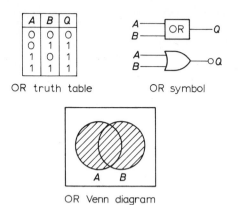

OR truth table

OR symbol

OR Venn diagram

Figure 6.2   Representations of the OR gate

6.4   Electronic logic levels

To make an electronic logic gate we must represent a (1) or a (0) by an electrical quantity such as a voltage. Figure 6.3 will help you to see how this is done. Four voltage levels are defined:

Zero, earth or ground   Usually the negative supply voltage.

The lower logic level (LLL)   A voltage just above ground, often 0.7 V.

The upper logic level (ULL)   A higher voltage, often $V_{CC}/2$.

The supply voltage V_{CC} Usually the positive supply rail.

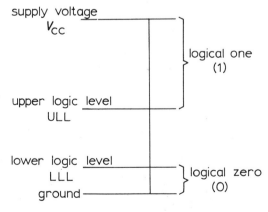

Figure 6.3   Electronic logic levels

Any voltage in the range zero to LLL is taken as logical zero (0). A voltage between the ULL and V_{CC} is represented by logical one (1). Circuits must be designed so that there are no voltages at input or output in the range LLL to ULL.

A logic system defined as described above is said to be using *positive logic*. If the supply leads were reversed so that V_{CC} was negative with respect to ground, we would be using *negative logic*. Either system is equally good, but we must not mix them.

6.5   The diode AND gate

Figure 6.4(a) shows the circuit of this gate together with a blank truth table. Figure 6.4(b), (c), (d) and (e) show the circuits produced when the inputs to the gate are connected as required by the truth table. By examining these circuits it is possible to work out the contents of the Q column.

Row 1 of the truth table is represented by Figure 6.4(b). Both inputs are connected to the negative rail, so making the inputs (0). The circuit therefore becomes a potential divider, with the voltage at Q equal to the voltage dropped across a forward-biased germanium diode, i.e. 0.2 V. This is below the LLL, and so the output Q is at (0). In Figure 6.4(c) (row 2 of table) the input B is (1) and so is moved to the positive rail. Here it is reversed biased and so can be ignored, leaving the output Q at (0). In Figure 6.4(d) (row 3 of table) the inputs are the other way round, with A this time reversed biased. Once again the output Q will be 0.2 V and so (0). In row 4 of the truth table both A and B are (1) and so are connected to the positive rail in Figure 6.4(e). Both diodes are reversed biased and so the resistor alone connects Q to the positive rail, making its voltage V_{CC} which is represented by (1).

The completed truth table is shown in Figure 6.4(f) and can be seen to be that for AND.

Note that if there is no connection made to an input this is equivalent to an input of (1).

6.6   The diode OR gate

Figure 6.5 follows the same pattern as Figure 6.4. Row 1 of the truth table gives a circuit in which two reverse-biased diodes are in parallel with a resistor connected to ground. Q is therefore at 0 V, i.e. (0). Rows 2 and 3 form a potential divider with one forward-biased diode. The diodes in this

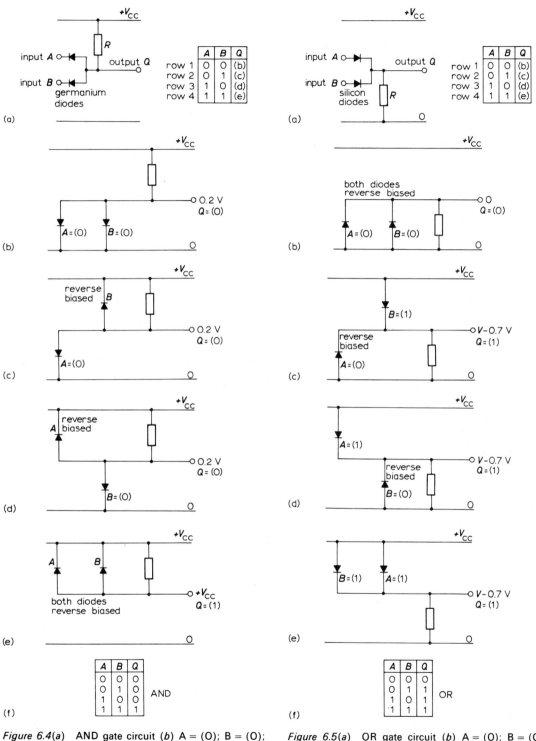

Figure 6.4(a) AND gate circuit (*b*) A = (O); B = (O); Q = (O), (*c*) A = (O); B = (1); Q = (O), (*d*) A = (1); B = (O); Q = (O), (*e*) A = (1); B = (1); Q = (1), (*f*) truth table for AND gate.

Figure 6.5(a) OR gate circuit (*b*) A = (O); B = (O); Q = (O), (*c*) A = (O); B = (1); Q = (1), (*d*) A = (1); B = (O); Q = (1), (*e*) A = (1); B = (1); Q = (1). (*f*) truth table for OR gate.

case are silicon, and so Q will be at a voltage 0.7 V below V_{CC}: that is, Q is (1). The circuit for row 4 has both diodes forward biased, but as they are in parallel they still drop only 0.7 V across them and Q remains at (1).

6.7   Problems with diode gates

A single diode gate is perfectly satisfactory, but in computers thousands of gates are connected end to end and this causes problems. Each time an AND is used the zero level is raised by 0.2 V and an OR gate lowers V_{CC} by 0.7 V. After a few gates the outputs will enter the forbidden region between the two logic levels. The problem is overcome, however, if the diode gates are combined with other gates which restore the outputs to their original values.

6.8   The NOT gate

In Section 6.1 three words were mentioned in connection with logical statements: AND, OR and NOT. NOT is used in statements such as 'John will NOT go to the cinema if Bill AND Fred are going.' The word NOT reverses the normal meaning of the AND condition. The truth table for this NOT AND or NAND condition is the AND truth table with the (1)s changed to (0)s and vice versa in the Q column (Figure 6.6).

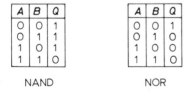

A	B	Q
0	0	1
0	1	1
1	0	1
1	1	0

NAND

A	B	Q
0	0	1
0	1	0
1	0	0
1	1	0

NOR

Figure 6.6   Truth tables and NAND and NOR gates

Statements like 'John will NOT use the car if his father OR mother want it' give rise to a condition of NOT OR or NOR. This has a truth table like that for OR with its Q column *complemented* – the correct word for exchanging (1)s and (0)s (Figure 6.6).

We can now see that to perform the NOT function electronically a circuit is required that will give a (1) output for a (0) input and vice versa. We do not have to invent such a circuit; it is

already a basic circuit, the inverter (see chapter 3). Figure 6.7 shows the inverter in its new role together with its symbol and truth table.

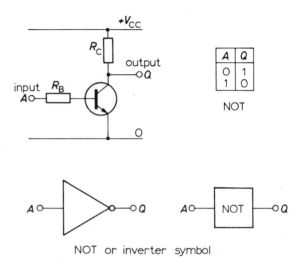

A	Q
0	1
1	0

NOT

NOT or inverter symbol

Figure 6.7   Inverter as NOT gate

6.9   The diode transistor NAND gate

We have an AND gate and a NOT, and so it should be possible to combine them to form a NAND. This is done in Figure 6.8. The resulting NAND circuit would work, but it is not the best that we can achieve. The original diode AND used germanium diodes and these are retained for Figure 6.8. The function of the diodes is to prevent a high input on one input reaching the other input, and this would be done best by silicon diodes which have very low leakage. The 0.7 V drop across silicon diodes, which is in the

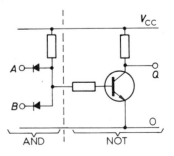

Figure 6.8   NAND gate circuit

opposite direction to the 0.7 V across the base/emitter junction, makes the transistor difficult to turn off. This can be cured by adding a forward-biased silicon diode in the base lead. The final circuit is shown in Figure 6.9. V_{CC} can have any value between 5 and 15 V.

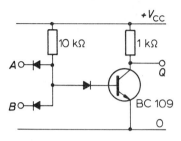

Figure 6.9 Practical NAND gate

The number of inputs that can be connected to a gate is called its *fan-in*. The NAND gate described above has a fan-in of two, but this can be increased to any desired number by adding extra diodes.

6.10 The diode transistor NOR gate

The result of adding a diode OR to an inverter is shown in Figure 6.10. You will notice that one of the resistors has been left out. V_{CC} can have any value between 5 and 15 V. Once again the fan-in can be increased by adding diodes.

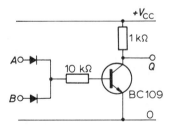

Figure 6.10 NOR gate circuit

The gates described in Sections 6.9 and 6.10 give rise to a family of logic gates called *diode transistor logic* (DTL).

6.11 Integrated logic circuits

Logic circuits are so widely used that several series of *integrated logic circuits* have been pro-

duced. An integrated circuit (IC) consists of a whole circuit or number of circuits manufactured on a single silicon chip one or two millimetres square. The circuits are produced on the silicon by repeating a sequence of operations:

- Oxidize the surface of the silicon.
- Etch 'windows' in the oxide.
- Diffuse donor or acceptor impurities in through the windows.
- Remove the oxide.

These are repeated over and over again until the components that form the circuits have been produced. Input and output leads are then joined to the chip and the chip is encapsulated in a plastic or ceramic material. A common encapsulation is known as *dual-in-line* and is illustrated in Figure 6.11. The two most common series of logic ICs, the 74 series and the CMOS (pronounced see moss) series, use dual-in-line encapsulation in the device formation.

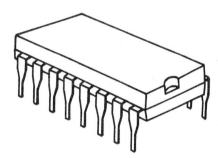

Figure 6.11 Dual-in-line encapsulation

The 74 *series* consists of a large number of logic ICs with an identification number starting with 74: for example, the 7400 contains four NAND gates. All 74 series gates are based on a logic family called *transistor transistor logic* (TTL). This is similar to DTL, but instead of separate diodes the base/emitter junctions of special multi-emitter transistors are used. The basic gate is the NAND, and the circuit of a TTL NAND is given in Figure 6.12.

Series 74 ICs will only operate correctly on a supply voltage of between 4.5 and 5.5 V, and a voltage of more than 7 V will destroy them. The gates are current sinking; no input is taken by the gate as an input of (1). Early 74 series chips contained only a few gates and were known as

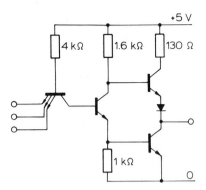

Figure 6.12 Circuit of TTL NAND gate

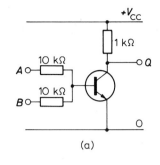

(a)

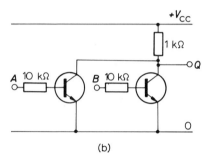

(b)

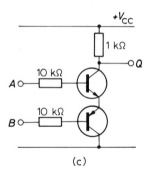

(c)

Figure 6.13 Alternative circuits (*a*) Resistor transistor logic NOR gate (*b*) Directly coupled transistor logic NOR gate (*c*) Directly coupled transistor logic NAND gate

small-scale integration. This has been followed by medium- and large-scale integration as more and more circuits are packed on to smaller and smaller chips.

The main advantage of TTL is its speed of operation, and its main disadvantage is the rigid power supply requirements. When large numbers of chips are used the large currents consumed are also a disadvantage, and even when using the new low-power Schottky chips supply currents of several amperes are common.

The *CMOS series* uses a kind of transistor construction called *metal oxide semiconductor* which allows closer packing of circuits, giving rise to very-large-scale integration. The gates will operate on any supply voltage between 3 V and 15 V, and they take very little current. The input resistance of CMOS gates is very high, which reduces loading on previous stages, but makes the gate subject to damage through static charge when handled. More information on these logic families is included in the summary at the end of this chapter.

6.12 Alternative circuits for NANDs and NORs

An alternative NOR circuit uses *resistor transistor logic* (RTL). Resistors are used instead of diodes to isolate the inputs from each other. Resistors are less effective but cheaper. The circuit is shown in Figure 6.13(a).

Figure 6.13(b) and (c) show another kind of logic known as *directly coupled transistor logic* (DCTL).

6.13 NAND and NOR equivalent circuits

The two inverting gates are particularly important because any other gate or system can be made from them. The designer of a logic system decides at the beginning if he is going to base his system on the NAND or on the NOR and then converts the whole system to a combination of the gate of his choice. Figure 6.14 shows the four gates we

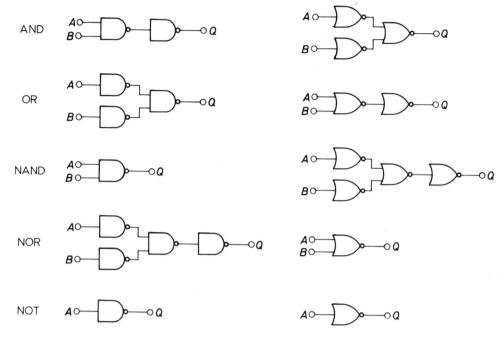

Figure 6.14 NAND and NOR equivalent circuits

have met so far and the combinations of NANDs and NORs which are equivalent to them. These combinations are often called the *De Morgan equivalents*. You will also notice in this figure that the inverter or NOT gate can be drawn as a single-input NAND or NOR.

The gates shown have as usual a fan-in of two. There is no reason why the fan-in cannot be increased, and a three-input OR gate made from NANDs is shown in Figure 6.15 together with its truth table.

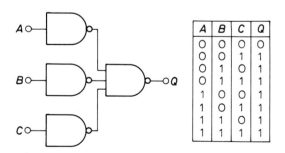

A	B	C	Q
0	0	0	0
0	0	1	1
0	1	0	1
0	1	1	1
1	0	0	1
1	0	1	1
1	1	0	1
1	1	1	1

Figure 6.15 Three-input OR gate made from NAND gates

Example '*A driver must wear a seat belt (S) whenever he is driving (D) unless he is reversing (R).*' *Convert this conditional statement to a logic system using NOR gates only.*

The statement can be summarized as

$$S \text{ if } D \text{ unless } R$$

This needs to be expressed another way if it is to be converted to gates. An alternative is

$$S \text{ if } D \text{ AND NOT } R$$

This is then drawn out using AND and NOT gates:

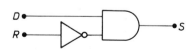

These gates are then replaced by their De Morgan equivalents:

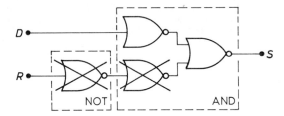

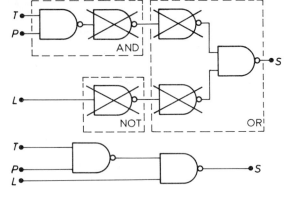

You will notice that the NOT is followed by another NOT gate. The input from R is therefore inverted twice, and so the two NOT gates in series form only an expensive piece of connecting wire and can be removed. The system is therefore reduced to two NOR gates:

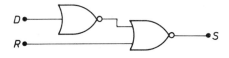

Example   *The boiler shut-down solenoid will operate if the temperature reaches 90 °C and the circulating pump is turned on, or if the pilot light goes out. Design a logic system to operate the boiler using NAND gates only.*

Let the boiler solenoid be S, the temperature reaching 90 °C be T, the pump on be P and the pilot light be L. The logic statement can now be summarized as

$$T \text{ and } P \text{ OR NOT } L.$$

This can then be converted to logic gates as shown:

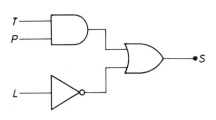

Each gate is then replaced by its De Morgan equivalent and any double inversions removed:

6.14   The exclusive-OR gate

In English, OR is an ambiguous word. Sometimes it means A OR B OR both A AND B, but at other times A AND B is excluded. The statement 'I will accept a five pound note OR five separate pounds' is of the first kind, and 'John will marry June OR Mary' is probably of the second. The second kind of OR is known as an exclusive-OR, and has its own symbol and truth table as shown in Figure 6.16.

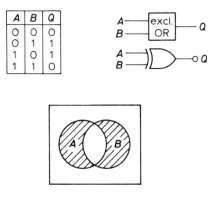

A	B	Q
0	0	0
0	1	1
1	0	1
1	1	0

Figure 6.16   Exclusive – OR gate

Like other gates and systems the exclusive-OR can be constructed out NANDs or NORs. From the truth table follows two ways of describing the action of the gate:

A OR *B* AND NOT *A* AND *B*

or   *A* AND NOT *B* OR *B* AND NOT *A*

These statements lead to two logic system for the gate:

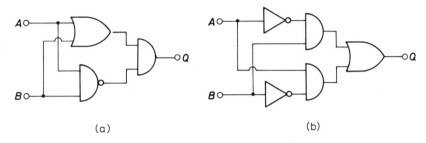

(a)   (b)

These can then be converted into NORs or NANDs:

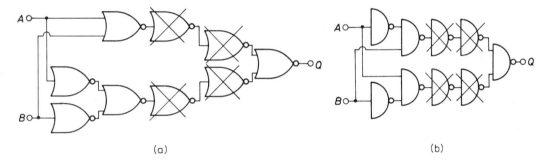

(a)   (b)

Any double inversions are then removed:

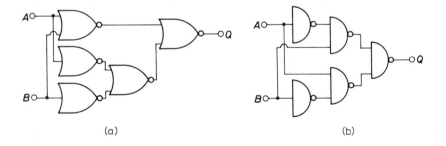

(a)   (b)

This leaves an exclusive-OR in NORs (a) and an exclusive-OR in NANDs (b).

6.15 The noise immunity of a gate

In electronics the term *noise* is used to describe the small random voltages produced by all electronic components when a current passes through them.

Imagine an inverter with its input connected to the zero line. There will be noise pulses on the line, and if one of these exceeds 0.7 V then the transistor will start to turn on. In this way it is possible for noise to introduce unintended (1)s into the system. Think what this would do if the inverter formed part of a computer. This danger could be reduced if the LLL of the gate was increased to 1.4 V by adding a forward-biased silicon diode in the base lead. Figure 6.17 shows the original and revised circuit. By adding the diode we have increased the *noise immunity* of the gate.

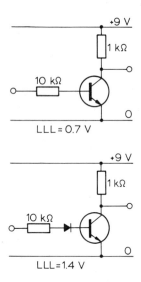

Figure 6.17   Increasing noise immunity of a gate

6.16   The fan-out of a gate

The *fan-out* of a gate is defined as the number of similar gates that can be driven from its output. This number is limited because too many gates would load the output and reduce the output voltage when set to (1) to below the upper logic level.

The fan-out of an inverter or gates based on it is roughly equal to the base resistor value divided by the collector resistor value. The fan-out of most TTL gates is 10, and CMOS gates have a fan-out of about 50.

6.17   Binary arithmetic

The terms logical one (1) and logical zero (0) have been used in the chapter so far as a way of describing high and low voltages, but inside the computer they form part of binary numbers.

The decimal system with which we are all familiar is an example of a *positional* number

system. A decimal number is made up of a series of *integers* from 0 to 9, and whether a particular integer 5 means 5 or 50 or 500 depends on its *position* in the number. For example, the number 376 means

$$3 \times 100$$
$$+7 \times 10$$
$$+6 \times 1$$

The binary system is also a positional system, but the integers are called *bits* and they can only be 1 or 0.

Starting at the right-hand end of a binary number, we find the *least significant bit* or LSB. A (1) in this position is multiplied by 1. Moving to the left bit by bit the multiplying factor doubles with each step, so that a (1) in the second position is multiplied by 2, in the third by 4 and so on until the end of the number is reached. The bit at the left-hand end is called the *most significant bit* or MSB. All this information is summarized by Figure 6.18.

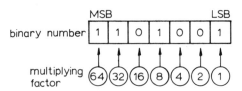

Figure 6.18   Binary number system

It follows that it is possible to work out the value of the decimal equivalent of a binary number by adding together the result of multiplying each bit by the multiplying factor given to its position. Consider the binary number 1101001 (as in Figure 6.18). Starting with the LSB,

$$
\begin{array}{rcl}
1 \times 1 & = & 1 \\
0 \times 2 & = & 0 \\
0 \times 4 & = & 0 \\
1 \times 8 & = & 8 \\
0 \times 16 & = & 0 \\
1 \times 32 & = & 32 \\
1 \times 64 & = & 64 \\
\hline
+ & & \\
\hline
& & 105
\end{array}
$$

Binary 1101001 is equivalent to decimal 105.

Note that the binary system needs more places than decimal to represent the same quantity. The lower efficiency of the binary system is accepted because of the practical advantages of only having to have two voltage levels. Imagine trying to design circuits which could have ten different output voltages!

Decimal numbers can be converted to binary by dividing by 2 over and over again and recording any remainders, as shown in the following example

---

Example   *Find the binary equivalent of* 247

$$247 \div 2 = 123 \quad \text{remainder 1}$$
$$123 \div 2 = 61 \quad \text{remainder 1}$$
$$61 \div 2 = 30 \quad \text{remainder 1}$$
$$30 \div 2 = 15 \quad \text{remainder 0}$$
$$15 \div 2 = 7 \quad \text{remainder 1}$$
$$7 \div 2 = 3 \quad \text{remainder 1}$$
$$3 \div 2 = 1 \quad \text{remainder 1}$$
$$1 \div 2 = 0 \quad \text{remainder 1}$$

The binary equivalent of 247 is 11110111.
   Check: 11110111 is

$$1 + 2 + 4 + 0 + 16 + 32 + 64 + 128 = 247$$

Counting in any number system consists of adding one over and over again. In the binary system each bit changes its state ((0) to (1) or (1) to (0)) when the bit on its right goes from (1) to (0), as shown in the table.

Binary number	Decimal equivalent
0000	0
0001	1
0010	2
0011	3
0100	4
0101	5
0110	6
0111	7
1000	8
1001	9
1010	10
1011	11
1100	12
1101	13
1110	14
1111	15

6.18 Combinational and sequential logic

In all the logic systems that we have met so far, the state of the output depends only on the state of the inputs. Systems like this are examples of *combinational logic*.

In some systems the state of the output depends not only on the present state of the inputs but on their past states as well. Systems like this are using *sequential logic*, and all must contain at least one circuit capable of 'remembering' past states.

The bistable latch of Section 5.12 and Figure 5.23 is such a circuit. Look at the bistable circuit in the light of the work on logic gates and you will see that it consists of two RTL NOR gates connected output to input. Figure 6.19(a) shows the bistable latch considered in this way, together with the table of Figure 5.24 in binary form. A set/reset (SR) bistable can be made by connecting a pair of NOR gates of any type in this way. The SR bistable will be set and reset by a logical (1).

It is also possible to make a SR bistable out of two NAND gates, when it will be set and reset by a logical (0) (Figure 6.19(b)).

6.19 The bistable register

In a computer all data and instructions are represented by binary numbers consisting of ones and zeros only. These numbers have to be stored, and this is done in a *register*.

A bistable has two stable states; one can be used to represent logical (1) and the other logical (0). When the Q output is (1) the bistable is storing (1), and the $\bar{Q}$ output is (1) when it is storing (0). A single bistable can store a single bit, therefore a row of bistables is able to store a complete binary number.

A row of bistables with their reset inputs connected together, so that all can be set to zero by a single pulse, forms a storage register. The set input of each bistable is connected to an AND gate as shown in Figure 6.20 so that information can only be set into the register when the input address line is (1). You will see that the outputs from the individual bistables are also routed through AND gates and controlled by an output address line.

Suppose we wanted to store the decimal number 13 in the register. The number $13 = 8 + 4$

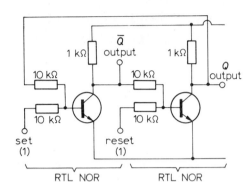

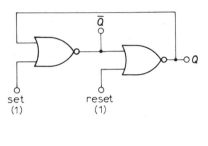

Set input	Reset input	Q output	$\bar{Q}$ output
1	1	0	0
1	0	1	0
0	1	0	1
0	0	remains in previous state	

Figure 6.19(a)   Bistable latch as a logic gate

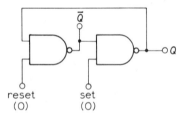

Figure 6.19(b)   Set/reset bistable from two NAND gates

+1, so we would need to put a (1) in the 8s bistable, a (1) in the 4s bistable, a (0) in the 2s bistable and a (1) in the 1s bistable. The stages required to do this are:

- Set all the bistables to (0) by making the reset line logical (1) for a short time.

- The correct binary number, 1 1 0 1, is now applied to the inputs of the input AND gates as shown in Figure 6.20.

- The bistables are now set to these states by making the input address line (1) for a short time.

If at any later time we need the information stored in this register, a (1) is applied to the output address line and the number 1 1 0 1 will appear on the outputs of the output AND gates.

6.20   The toggle bistable

The usefulness of an SR bistable can be greatly increased if a *toggle* input is added. When the state of this input goes from (0) to (1) or vice versa, the state of the bistable's outputs are changed. That is, if the Q output is at (1) it is changed to (0), and if at (0) it is changed to (1). With this input the circuit becomes a T-type bistable.

Figure 6.21 shows a transistor version of this bistable. The two 22 kΩ resistors sense the states of the outputs, the diodes stop one output affecting the other, and the capacitors transfer voltage pulses to the transistor bases so that the state of the bistable is changed. The circuit changes state when the T input goes from (1) to (0).

Imagine that Q is at (1), a voltage of V_{CC}, and $\bar{Q}$ is at (0). With T held at (1) the right-hand capacitor will have V_{CC} on its lower plate and 0.7 V on its upper plate. The left-hand capacitor will have 0 V on both plates. When T changes to (0) it will have no effect on the left-hand capacitor, but the bottom plate of the right-hand one will be suddenly pulled down to 0.7 V. The voltage across a capacitor cannot suddenly change, as time is taken for charge to flow. Therefore the voltage on the upper plate will also

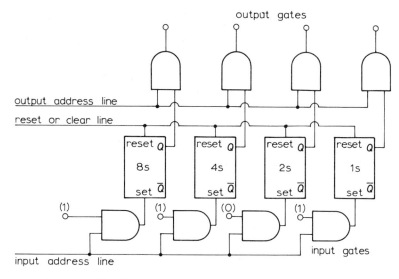

Figure 6.20 Storage register using bistables

fall, taking the base of the left-hand transistor with it and so turning it off. $\bar{Q}$ then becomes (1) and Q becomes (0), leaving the bistable to change in the opposite direction the next time T goes from (1) to (0). The change from (0) to (1) in between will have no effect.

The version of the T-type bistable described is used today only when a single bistable is required and the rest of the system consists of transistor circuits. In other situations one of the multipurpose integrated circuit bistables described below would give a cheaper and more reliable solution.

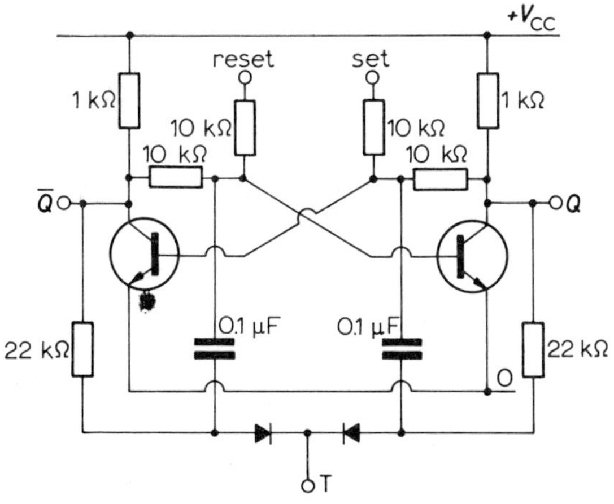

6.21 The D-type bistable

The D-type bistable has the usual connections of Q and $\bar{Q}$ outputs and S and R inputs, but in addition it has a *clock* input and a *data* input.

Each time the clock input changes state (in some it is (1) to (0), and in others (0) to (1)) the state of the D input is transferred to the Q output. Figure 6.22 shows a D-type with its $\bar{Q}$ output connected to its D input. Let us suppose that the D is transferred to Q when the C input goes (1) to (0). This is called *negative-going edge triggering*. Output $\bar{Q}$ is always opposite to Q, and so D is always in the state opposite to Q. Each time C is

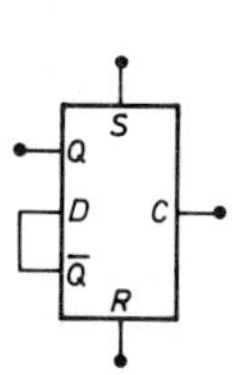

Figure 6.21 Transistor T-type bistable

Figure 6.22 D-type bistable

triggered, Q will change its state and the circuit will behave exactly like a T-type bistable.

Several D-type bistables are included in both the 74 series and in CMOS. The 74LS74 is a TTL low-power chip containing two identical D-types. They are *positive-going edge triggered*, i.e. they change state when the clock goes from (0) to (1). The 4013B is a CMOS dual D-type which is also triggered on the positive-going edge of the clock pulse. The pin connections of these and other 74 series and CMOS gates are given at the end of the chapter.

6.22   The JK bistable

This bistable has connections $Q, \bar{Q}, S, R, J, K,$ and C (Figure 6.23).

- If both J and K are (1), the bistable becomes a T-type and changes state on each clock pulse.

- If J is (1) and K is (0), the output Q is set to (1).

- If J is (0) and K is (1), the output Q is set to (0).

- If both J and K are (0), the output remains in its present state.

In the 74 series an input left unconnected is the equivalent of an input of (1). Therefore if the J and K inputs are left unconnected, the bistable becomes a T-type.

Figure 6.23   JK bistable

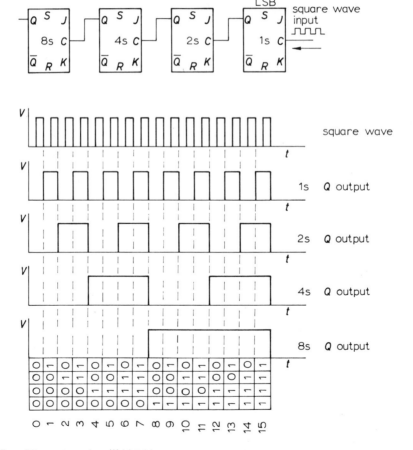

Figure 6.24   Four-bit counter using JK bistables

The 74LS76 is a TTL chip containing two JK bistables. The bistables change state when the clock goes from (1) to (0). The 4027B is a dual CMOS JK bistable which triggers on the rising edge of the clock pulse.

6.23 The binary counter

If you read again the conditions for binary counting in Section 6.17 you will see that they are met by the transistor T-type bistable of Section 6.20 and also by a 74LS76 JK bistable. In either bistable the output Q changes state when an input connected to C or T changes from (1) to (0). If the clock or toggle input is joined to the Q output of the bistable to its right, a counter will be formed.

A four-bit counter made out of JK bistables is shown in Figure 6.24. This figure also contains a set of graphs. The top graph shows the variation with time of a square-wave voltage applied to the C input of the bistable representing the LSB. Lower graphs show the voltage variations at the Q outputs of the other bistables. Below the graphs are shown the binary numbers representing each state of the counter and the decimal equivalents.

Suppose we now joined a number of 74LS74 D-type bistables with Q output to C exactly as we connected the JK bistables. Assuming that we started with all the bistables reset to zero, the result of applying a square wave to the LSB input is shown in Figure 6.25. Remember that this particular D-type triggers when its clock goes from (0) to (1), i.e. on the positive-going edge of the clock pulse.

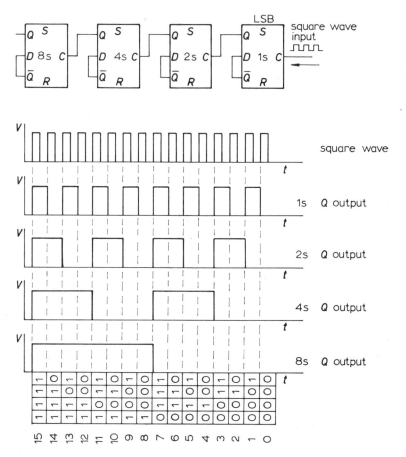

Figure 6.25 Four-bit counter using D-type bistables

You will notice from the graphs that this counter is counting in binary but backwards. A counter of this kind is called a *down counter*, the ordinary one being of course an *up counter*. For some applications a down counter can be very useful, but suppose we wanted an up counter and we wanted to use the 74LS74. Whenever the Q output is going from (0) to (1) the $\bar{Q}$ output is moving in the opposite direction. If the counter is connected $\bar{Q}$ to C instead of Q to C, it will therefore function as an up counter. Similarly the 74LS76 counter can be turned into a down counter by joining $\bar{Q}$ to C. You may well feel rather confused, but the following summary should help:

	Up counter	Down counter
Bistable changes state as its clock goes from (0) to (1) Positive-going edge triggering.	$\bar{Q}$ to next C	Q to next C
Bistable changes state as its clock goes from (1) to (0). Negative-going edge triggering.	Q to next C	$\bar{Q}$ to next C

The square wave applied to the LSB of a binary counter consists of a number of square pulses called *clock pulses*, and it is these pulses that are being counted.

Another way of looking at the counter is to think of it as a *frequency divider*. The original square wave has a particular frequency equal to the number of clock pulses produced per second, and this frequency is divided by 2 for each bistable in the counter. Our four-bit counter can therefore be called a *divide-by-sixteen* counter. You will see from the graphs that on some clock pulses each of the bistables in the counter changes state in turn. It is as though the effect of the clock pulse 'rippled through' the bistables, and for this reason this type of circuit is called a *ripple-through* counter. This is the only kind of counter described in this book, but you should note that the delay while the changes ripple through makes the counter too slow for some applications.

6.24   Uses of the binary counter

Uses of the binary counter can be grouped under three headings:

(1) Finding the total number of a sequence of individual events. For example, a light beam and a detector could be set up across a doorway so that each time a person entered the door a clock pulse was generated. In this way the number of people entering the door in a given time could be found.

(2) Dividing time up into a number of equal intervals so that a number of operations that take place in a sequence can be allocated different times. For example, in a traffic light sequence the lights are not all illuminated for the same time. If we used our divide-by-sixteen counter we could make RED be on for seven clock pulses, RED and AMBER for one, GREEN for seven and AMBER alone for one, so adding up to sixteen.

(3) Arranging for a number of operations to take place in a particular order. An obvious example is the traffic light sequence described above, but a more interesting one can be found inside the control area of any computer. A computer has to carry out a large number of operations, and it is vital that they are carried out in the correct order. All computers have an oscillator or clock which drives a counter to do this.

6.25   Decoding a counter

Suppose that, in an example of use type (3), a particular operation had to be carried out when the counter reached 5. We must use a logic gate to detect when this count has been reached, and the output from the gate can start the operation.

The obvious gate to choose is the AND gate. Its output will be (1) only when all its inputs are (1). Figure 6.26(a) shows this arrangement. A three-bit counter will be needed as five is between four and eight. Note that the inputs to the AND gate go to the Q outputs of the outer bistables but to the $\bar{Q}$ output of the centre bistable. This is because the number 5 in binary is 101.

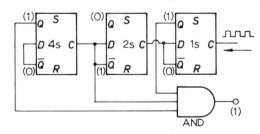

Figure 6.26(a)   Decoding a counter

From the electronic engineer's point of view, the AND is not the best gate to use. The circuits for NANDs and NORs are more simple. Figures 6.26(b) and (c) show how these gates can be used. With the NAND version the output from the gate will be (0) only on the count of 5, and in the NOR version the connections to Q and $\bar{Q}$ are reversed. Whatever gate is used, the process of detecting a particular state of a counter is called *decoding*.

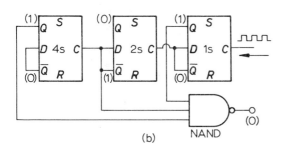

(b) NAND

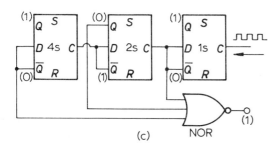

(c) NOR

Figure 6.26(b) and (c) Improved decoders

6.26 The decade counter

The decade counter is a binary counter which counts normally up to 9 but resets itself to zero when it reaches count 10. It therefore has ten states, 0 to 9, and so is a divide-by-10 counter. Ten is between 8 and 16, so we will need a four-bit counter. Suppose we are going to use two 74LS74 dual D-type bistables. These counters trigger on the positive-going edge of the clock pulse and reset with a (0). Binary ten is 1 0 1 0, and we should decode this with a four-input NAND. Figure 6.27 shows the complete counter.

In most applications where a binary counter is used to count objects or events, the result will have to be read by human beings and they find binary rather difficult. One NAND gate can decode any particular state in a counter. There-

fore ten NAND gates could be used to decode all the states of a decade counter and give a decimal output. The output from a decade counter is in binary-coded decimal or BCD, and the set of ten NAND gates forms a *BCD-to-decimal decoder*. Counters and decoders of this type exist as integrated circuits in both the 74 series and the CMOS family.

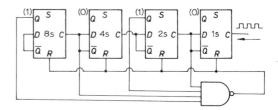

Figure 6.27 Decade counter made from 74LS74 D-type bistables

6.27 The seven-segment display

It is not enough to just decode the ten decimal states: they have to be displayed as readable decimal digits. Many attempts have been made to do this, but the most common is the *seven-segment display*. The display consists of seven bar-shaped segments, which can be illuminated if required, arranged in the form of a square eight. Figure 6.28 shows how different combinations of segments can be illuminated to form the digits 0 to 9.

To drive a seven-segment display from a decimal decoder, we would have to connect each of the decimal outputs to the appropriate segments. A little thought shows that then all the segments will be joined together and all will light up for every number. To avoid this a diode must be placed in each lead so that it is forward biased. These diodes form a *diode matrix* as shown in Figure 6.29. Integrated BCD-to-seven-segment decoder/drivers are available that can drive a common-cathode LED display directly. These are the 74 series 74LS48 and the CMOS 4511B. In a common cathode display all the segments are individual LEDs and their cathodes are connected together. The common cathode goes to earth and the seven anodes are connected to the decoder outputs through resistors. Resistors of 220 Ω are suitable for a 5 V supply. The 74LS47 drives a common-anode display where all the anodes are connected to V_{CC}.

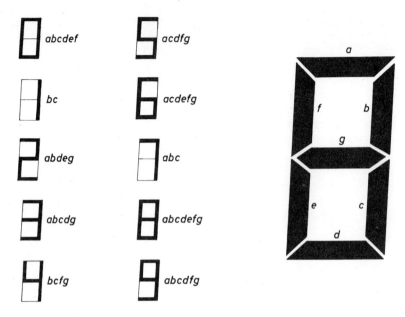

Figure 6.28 Seven-segment display

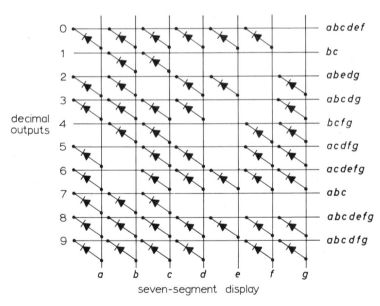

Figure 6.29 Diode matrix to drive seven-segment display

Summary

Logic gates

Gate	Truth table	Symbol	NOR equivalent	NAND equivalent

NOR

A	B	Q
0	0	1
0	1	0
1	0	0
1	1	0

OR

A	B	Q
0	0	0
0	1	1
1	0	1
1	1	1

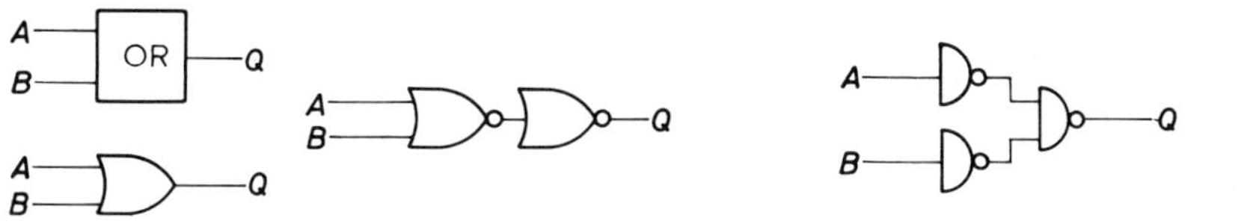

AND

A	B	Q
0	0	0
0	1	0
1	0	0
1	1	1

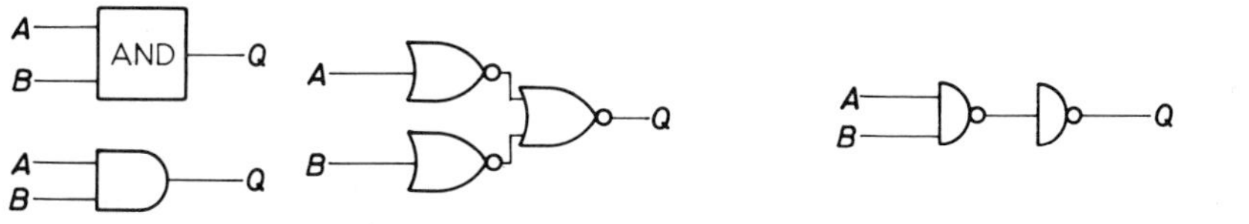

NAND

A	B	Q
0	0	1
0	1	1
1	0	1
1	1	0

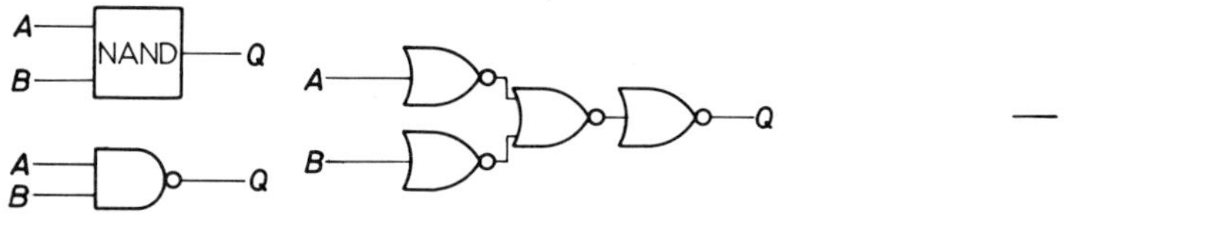

NOT invert

A	Q
0	1
1	0

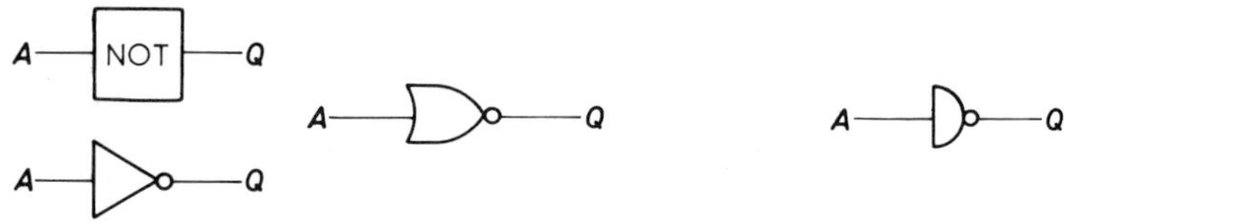

exclusive-OR

A	B	Q
0	0	0
0	1	1
1	0	1
1	1	0

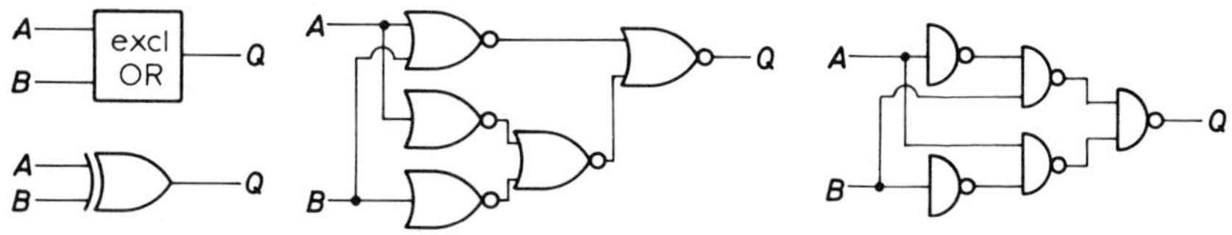

D-type bistable

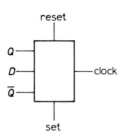

To convert to a toggle bistable, join D to $\bar{\bar{Q}}$.

JK bistable

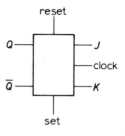

To convert to a toggle bistable, leave J and K unconnected or connect to logical (1).

Basic circuits

NAND gate

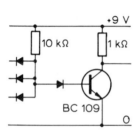

The output will only be (0) if all the inputs are (1).

Any of the TTL or CMOS logic families can be considered as ready built basic circuits to combine with the other circuits in this book. A selection of some of the most useful are shown here.

Logic ICs are not always as simple to use as they appear. When using TTL you must have a good regulated 5 V supply, and connect the supply lines by 100 nF capacitors every few gates. In either family, if your counter or decoder appears to be faulty, look for pins that have to be tied to the positive or negative line before the chip will work.

NOR gate

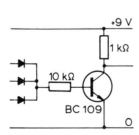

The output will only be (1) if all the inputs are (0).

Toggle bistable

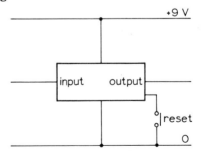

Output voltage changes state, (1) or (0), each time input goes from high to low. Negative edge triggering. Use CMOS D-type or JK flip-flop.

The 74 series of TTL integrated circuits

Supply voltage 5 V.
Upper logic level 2 V.

Lower logic level 0.8 V.
Unconnected inputs equivalent to input of (1).

7400 quadruple two-input NAND gate

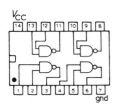

7402 quadruple two-input NOR gate

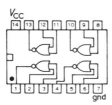

7404 hexadecimal inverter

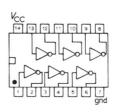

7408 quadruple two-input AND gate

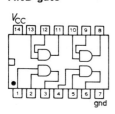

7410 triple three-input NAND gate

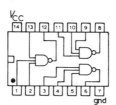

7414 hexadecimal Schmitt trigger

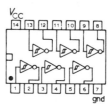

7474 dual D-type edge-triggered flip-flop

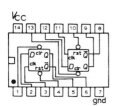

7475 quadruple bistable latch

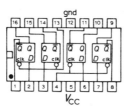

7476 dual JK master-slave flip-flop with preset and clear

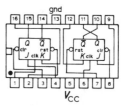

7420 dual four-input NAND gate

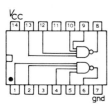

7430 eight-input NAND gate

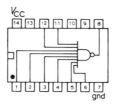

7442 BCD-to-decimal decoder

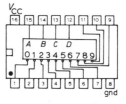

7490 decade counter

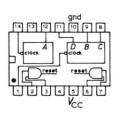

7493 four-bit binary counter

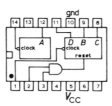

7447 BCD-to-seven-segment decoder/driver

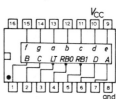

CMOS 4000B series

Positive supply V_{DD} 3 V to 18 V.
Negative supply V_{SS}.
Upper logic level is 0.7 V_{DD}.

Lower logic level is 0.3 V_{DD}.
All unused inputs must be tied to V_{DD} or V_{SS}.

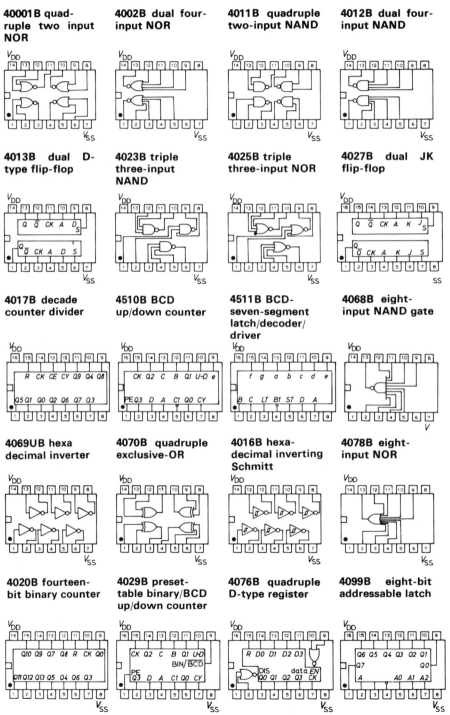

Questions

1 Name and give the symbol for the logic gates which can be represented by the following diagrams:

A	B	Q
0	0	1
0	1	0
1	0	0
1	1	0

(a)

(b)

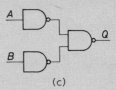

(c)

2 'The bank safe can only be opened (*Q*) by the manager (*M*) AND the cashier (*C*) OR the cashier AND a director (*D*).'
Represent this statement by a number of logic gates combined together (a) using any kind of gate (b) using only NOR gates. (c) using only NAND gates. In (b) and (c), simplify if possible.
Hint: There are two ways of looking at this statement: choose the right ones and it can be reduced to three NORs or three NANDs.

3 If *D* represents drinking, *C* represents driving and *Q* represents 'allowed by law', draw a truth table for the statement 'If you drink you must not drive.'
What single logic gate represents this statement?

4 You have two switch units, each of which can switch its output from logical (0) to logical (1). You also have four electrical appliances – a radio, a TV set, a hi-fi unit and a tape recorder – each of which can be switched on by applying a logical (1) to its input. Show how you could use a number of logic gates to control all four appliances by the two switches.

5 'There will be an electronics club meeting on the 10th of every month provided that the hall is available and the lecturer can attend, unless the 10th falls on a Saturday or a Sunday.'
Represent this statement by a system of NOR gates.

6 'The Army will accept you if you have belonged to the college CCF or you can pass this test unless your health is poor.'
Represent each of the conditions in this statement by an input such that the input is (1) if the condition is present. Design a logic system for the statement using only NAND gates.

7 'The successful applicant for this position will have two of the following qualifications: experience in direct selling; ability to drive; five O levels.
This is an ambiguous statement. What happens if the candidate has all three? Using any gates, design logic systems for both possible meanings.

8 Write down truth tables and possible statements for the logic systems shown.

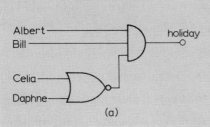

(a)

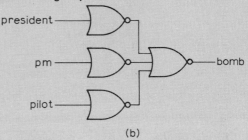

(b)

9 Write out a truth table for this logic system, and draw another system which satisfies the same truth table consisting of NAND gates only.

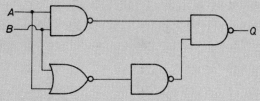

10 A, B and C are three input signals to a control system, and Q is the output. The truth table shows the desired function of the system.

Draw the simplest logic system using (a) NOR gates only (b) NAND gates only that will satisfy this function.

A	B	C	Q
0	0	0	1
1	0	0	1
0	1	0	0
0	0	1	0
1	1	0	1
0	1	1	0
1	0	1	0
1	1	1	1

11 Describe the working of the system shown, and sketch a graph showing the form of the current which flows through the loudspeaker.

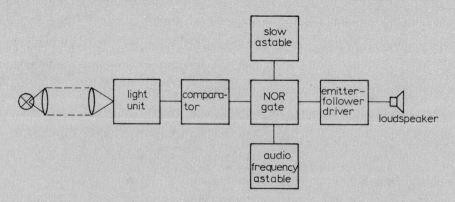

12 Describe the working of the system shown.

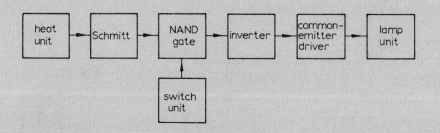

If the thermistor heated is represented by (1), the switch closed by (1) and the lamp on by (1), draw a truth table showing the condition of the lamp for the various combinations of input.

Basic amplifier circuits

7.1 Amplifier types

The term *Amplifier* usually refers to an electronic circuit with an input and an output, in which one of the electrical quantities of the input is increased at the output. In a voltage amplifier the quantity is voltage, so that the *gain* of the amplifier can be defined by

$$\text{voltage gain} = \frac{\text{output voltage}}{\text{input voltage}} = A_v$$

In a similar way,

$$\text{current gain} = \frac{\text{output current}}{\text{input current}} = A_i$$

and

$$\text{power gain} = \frac{\text{output power}}{\text{input power}} = G_p$$

As power = current × voltage

$$G_p = A_i A_v$$

We can therefore talk about voltage amplifiers, current amplifiers and power amplifiers. However, when we use the word 'amplifier' without saying which type we mean, it is taken as being a voltage amplifier.

Amplifiers can also be divided into direct current (DC) and alternating current (AC). The kind of amplifiers that we come upon in our ordinary lives, in our radios and record players, are AC amplifiers, and it is with this type that the chapter will begin. First we must be clear what is meant by AC.

7.2 Alternating currents and voltages

All the currents flowing in the circuits of Chapters 5 and 6 have been direct: that is, they have flowed in one direction only, toward earth, even though their magnitude may have varied.

Figure 7.1 shows three graphs of direct currents. Graph (a) is of a current produced by a steady voltage source such as a battery. Graph (b) shows an exponentially declining current of the type flowing into a capacitor as it charges. Graph

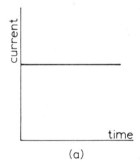

(a)

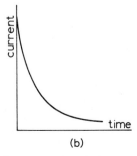

(b)

Figure 7.1(a) Current produced by steady voltage source (*b*) Exponentially declining current

(c) is of a current pulse as produced by a monostable. What the three graphs have in common is that they are always positive, meaning that the current is always flowing in the same direction.

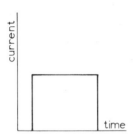

Figure 7.1(c)   Current pulse as produced by monostable

In an alternating current the graph will go below as well as above the line, indicating that the current flows in both directions, and the graph will cross the time axis at regular intervals. The time interval between the line crossing the axis in the same direction is called the *period* of the alternating current. The shape of an alternating current is the same during each period, and the number of times this shape is repeated each second is called the *frequency*.

$$\text{frequency} = \frac{1}{\text{period}} \qquad f = \frac{1}{T}$$

The unit of frequency is the hertz (Hz).

Figure 7.2 shows several alternating waveforms. The waveforms usually have descriptive names as shown, but the name of one, the sine wave, is less obvious, as it is the shape obtained when the graph of $I' = I_0 \sin 2\pi ft$ is plotted. The importance of the sine wave stems from a French mathematician called Jean Fourier, who in 1880 showed that *any* periodic waveform could be considered as the sum of a number of sine waves. This means that instead of having to study the infinity of differing possible waveforms, we only have to study sine waves.

A particular sine wave can be completely described by giving its frequency and the greatest amount by which it deviates from zero in either direction – its *amplitude*. To produce an alternating current in a resistor requires a voltage of the same frequency and waveform. In an AC voltage

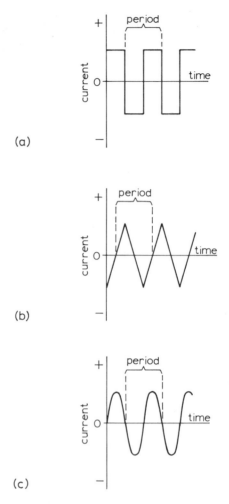

(a)

(b)

(c)

Figure 7.2   Alternating waveforms (*a*) Square wave (*b*) Triangle wave (*c*) Sine wave

amplifier a *sinusoidal* (sine-wave) voltage is applied to the input and, if the amplifier has been correctly designed, a similar sinusoidal voltage will be obtained from the output.

7.3   The inverter as an amplifier

Now that we know what is expected from an AC voltage amplifier, we can try to design one. The inverter is a very simple circuit but it is a good starting point for amplifier design.

Figure 7.3 shows an inverter with a sinusoidal voltage applied to its input and a CRO connected between its output and the zero line. Our task is to work out what will appear on the CRO screen. Refer back to Section 3.10 and particularly

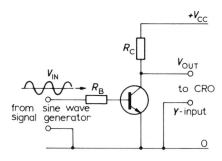

Figure 7.3 Inverter as an amplifier

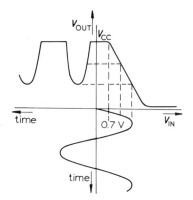

Figure 7.5

Figure 3.16(c). The input/output voltage characteristic shown in the figure is repeated in Figure 7.4. In addition, sharing the v_{IN} axis is a graph of the input voltage applied to the inverter plotted against time.

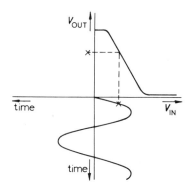

Figure 7.4 Voltage characteristic of inverter

On the v_{OUT} axis can be plotted a graph showing the shape of the output, also against time. It is the last graph that will be displayed on the CRO. Drawing the three graphs together in this way makes it possible to work out the shape of the output by drawing. To find a point on the output graph, select a point on the input graph and note its time. Draw a line vertically upward until it reaches the voltage characteristic, and then horizontally. The point on the output graph is where this line cuts a vertical through the corresponding time on the output graph. One output point is plotted in Figure 7.4. Try to work out the shape of the output for yourself, and then look at Figure 7.5 where the graph is completed.

You will see that the inverter as it stands does not make a perfect amplifier. Half of the input

wave has been amplified, but half has been lost. How can the circuit be modified so that the whole input signal is amplified? The input voltage needs to be moved to the right so that its centre lies under the centre of the sloping part of the voltage characteristic, and its amplitude must be reduced. The circuit now operates correctly as shown in Figure 7.6. To move the input signal requires the addition of a direct voltage called *bias* to the AC signal. The bias voltage is shown as V_B on the graph, and a way in which a battery of EMF V_B could be used to provide this bias is also shown.

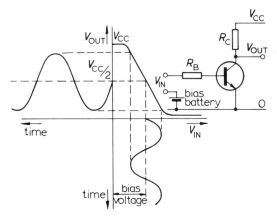

Figure 7.6 Inverting amplifier with bias

You will notice that as the input voltage rises, the output voltage falls. The circuit is an *inverting amplifier* – no surprise for a circuit based on an inverter.

What can be said about the gain of the amplifier?

$$\text{voltage gain} = \frac{\text{peak output voltage}}{\text{peak input voltage}}$$

$$= \text{slope of active region of}$$
$$\text{characteristic}$$

The steeper we can make the slope of the voltage characteristic, the greater voltage gain will be obtained from the amplifier. The easiest way of making the graph steeper is to reduce R_B. It is not possible to make the line vertical and so obtain infinite gain, even by reducing R_B to zero. The transistor itself acts as if a resistor r_{IN} remained, where

$$r_{IN} = \frac{0.025 \, h_{FE}}{I_C}$$

This gives a maximum slope and so a maximum value for the voltage gain:

$$A_v = \frac{\text{output voltage}}{\text{input voltage}} = \frac{I_c R_c}{I_B r_{IN}} = \frac{h_{FE} R_c}{r_{IN}} = \frac{I_c R_c}{0.025}$$

It is also possible to calculate a rough value for this maximum voltage gain by using the equation

$$A_v = V_{CC} \, 20$$

Look again at the graph of Figure 7.6. The amplifier is not working quite as well as we thought. The original input was a sine wave which varied an equal distance either side of zero. To this input a bias voltage was added, but nevertheless the correct output would be a larger sine wave varying either side of zero. In fact we have a larger amplitude sine wave varying either side of $\frac{1}{2}V_{CC}$. In other words, the output has a bias of $\frac{1}{2}V_{CC}$.

7.4   Current biasing an amplifier

The bias battery of Figure 7.6 is not a practical solution to the problem of biasing an amplifier. Resistors would be a cheaper solution, but any solution using resistors runs into a further problem. Consider the circuit of Figure 7.7. If the value for R_B was carefully calculated so that the output voltage with no input was exactly $\frac{1}{2}V_{CC}$, the bias would be correct. The current flowing into the transistor would be just enough to turn it half on:

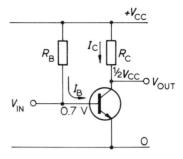

Figure 7.7   Current-biased transistor amplifier

$$I_C = \frac{\frac{1}{2}V_{CC}}{R_C} \qquad I_B = \frac{I_C}{h_{FE}}$$

$$R_B = \frac{V_{CC} - 0.7}{I_B}$$

The transistor is *current biased.*

As soon as the input was connected to the amplifier, however, the bias would be upset. Any source of alternating voltage, like any voltage source, must have a resistance of its own; this would allow a flow to earth of some of the current that was supposed to go into the transistor. We need a device that will allow the AC signal to enter the amplifier but will block the flow of direct current. Refer this time to Section 1.15. You will find that a capacitor will let AC flow through it but it will block DC. A capacitor used in this way is called a *coupling capacitor*, and is shown in Figure 7.8(a).

Another disadvantage of the simple current-biased amplifier is that to calculate R_B an exact value for h_{FE} is required, and this can only be obtained by measurement on the particular transistor used. Figure 7.8(b) shows a way in which this disadvantage can be overcome. In this current-biased circuit only an approximate value for h_{FE} is required. If the actual value is larger than this the transistor will turn on too much, making the output voltage lower than $\frac{1}{2}V_{CC}$, which in turn will reduce I_B, and so the bias will stabilize at a voltage only a little below $\frac{1}{2}V_{CC}$. What will happen if h_{FE} is too small? The design equations are now

$$I_C = \frac{\frac{1}{2}V_{CC}}{R_C} \qquad I_B = \frac{I_C}{h_{FE}}$$

$$R_B \frac{\frac{1}{2}V_{CC} - 0.7}{I_B}$$

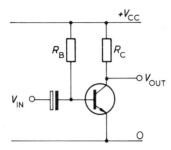

Figure 7.8(a)

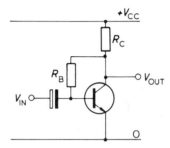

Figure 7.8(b) Current-biased amplifier with negative feedback

This circuit is using DC negative feedback through R_B to stabilize the bias. It is *negative feedback* because the amplifier *inverts*. Both AC and DC can flow through a resistor, and so, as well as the DC negative feedback that we want, we get unwanted AC negative feedback which reduces the gain of the amplifier. The loss in gain, however, is worth trading for the stability of bias obtained.

Example   *Design a common-emitter AC voltage amplifier to operate from a supply voltage of 9 V and using a current of about 5 mA.*

If the amplifier is correctly biased with its output voltage at $\frac{1}{2}V_{CC}$, the voltage across R_C will be 4.5 V. If R_C is made 1 kΩ, this will give a current of about 5 mA as required. Actual $I_C = 4.5$ mA, so

$$I_B = \frac{4.5}{200} = 0.0225 \text{ mA}$$

assuming that the average gain of the transistor type used is 200.

Then

$$R_B = \frac{4.5 - 0.7}{0.0225} = 170 \text{ k}\Omega$$

The nearest preferred value is 180 kΩ.

The action of the current-biased amplifier has been studied in some detail, but of course it is not necessary to go into this detail in order to use the circuit. The circuit designed in the previous example can simply be added to our list of basic circuits, and is illustrated as such in Figure 7.9.

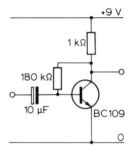

Figure 7.9 Practical current-biased amplifier

7.5 Voltage biasing an amplifier

Another solution to the problem of biasing a common-emitter amplifier is to set the voltage at the base to a suitable value by means of a potential divider. The circuit is shown in Figure 7.10(a). Once again the simple solution proves to be too simple. The bias voltage required would be about 0.7 V, but its exact value would vary from transistor to transistor and the vari-

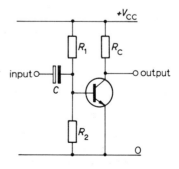

Figure 7.10(a) Voltage-biased amplifier

ation would be enough to upset the bias. The answer is to add an emitter resistor as in Figure 7.10(b), which gives both AC and DC negative feedback. The DC feedback gives us stable bias, and the AC reduces the voltage gain, this time to R_C/R_E. The final basic circuit is shown in Figure 7.10(c), where the emitter resistor is bypassed by a large electrolytic *decoupling capacitor* which removes the AC negative feedback and restores the gain to $20V_{CC}$. In the circuit illustrared the emitter resistor is a potentiometer with the decoupling capacitor joined to its slider. The gain can therefore be varied between R_C/R_E and $20\ V_{CC}$.

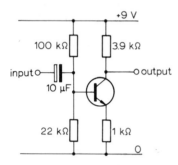

Figure 7.10(b)   Voltage-biased amplifier with negative feedback

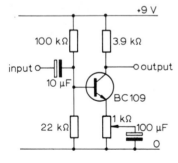

Figure 7.10(c)   Voltage-biased amplifier with negative feedback and decoupling capacitor

7.6   An opamp inverting AC amplifier

It is a simple matter to design an opamp version of the voltage-biased amplifier. One forms an important basic circuit and is shown in Figure 7.11(a). The non-inverting input is biased to $\frac{1}{2}V_{CC}$ by the two 1 kΩ resistors, and the very high

open-loop voltage gain of the opamp is reduced by negative feedback through resistors R_F and R_{IN}. These last two resistors define the gain of the amplifier, its closed-loop gain, as R_F/R_{IN}. Note the use of the coupling capacitor to isolate the input from any DC offsets.

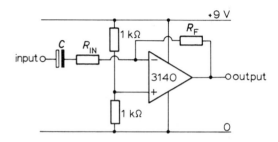

Figure 7.11(a)   Opamp version of voltage-biased amplifier

In use an amplifier is always driven from some previous circuit or transducer, and we must beware of loading it. The same rule, the rule of ten, applies to amplifiers as to potential dividers, but instead of talking about resistance we use the term *impedance*, which applies to AC circuits as well as to DC. The rule of ten then states that the input impedance of an amplifier must be at least ten times the output impedance of the device or circuit that drives it. Impedance, like resistance, is measured in ohms. The input impedance of the inverting opamp amplifier is equal to R_{IN}. The transistor amplifiers of the previous sections have input impedances of about 1 kΩ. Referring to the circuit of Figure 7.11(b), you will see that the input impedance is 10 kΩ and the voltage gain is variable between 1 and 100.

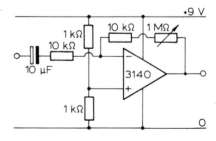

Figure 7.11(b)

The amplifier described above will be the one you will want to use for most purposes, but sometimes you may require a DC amplifier. These amplifiers give a steady output voltage when a steady input voltage is applied to them. If a voltage of 1 V was applied to the input of a DC inverting amplifier of voltage gain 10, we would expect an output voltage of − 10 V.

It is possible to convert the circuit of Figure 7.11(a) to a DC amplifier simply by removing the coupling capacitor. You must remember, however, that the amplifier has been biased to $\frac{1}{2}V_{CC}$, and so input and output voltage must be measured relative to this voltage. With a 9 V supply, $\frac{1}{2}V_{CC} = 4.5$ V, and so an input of 4 V is regarded by the opamp as an input of − 0.5 V. If the gain of the amplifier was 5, the output would be 7 V (5 × 0.5 = 2.5 V and 4.5 + 2.5 = 7 V). To avoid this arithmetic it is usual to use a split power supply with DC amplifiers, when all voltages are relative to earth (see Figure 7.12). Beware of combining amplifiers using split power supplies with those operating on a single-ended supply. Power supplies are often left out of dual-supply circuits to avoid confusion. Inputs and outputs are assumed to be measured relative to earth.

7.7 An opamp non-inverting amplifier

To convert the inverting amplifier to one that does not invert its output, it is only necessary to exchange the input and the bias point. The resulting circuit is illustrated in Figure 7.13(a). Note that two 220 kΩ resistors have been added. This is because the input impedance into the non-inverting input of an opamp is so high that the coupling capacitor has no route to discharge and so will not 'conduct' the AC correctly. The resistors make the input impedance 100 kΩ.

You will notice that circuits of Figures 7.13(b) and (c) are dual-power-supply DC versions, and look more simple than the single-ended AC version of Figure 7.13(a). Looking at circuit (c) it is clear that a proportion of the output determined by the potential divider formed by R_1 and R_2 is fed back into the inverting input, i.e. negative feedback. The fraction fed back is $R_2/(R_1 + R_2)$, and the closed-loop voltage gain of the amplifier is given by

$$A_v = \frac{R_1 + R_2}{R_2}$$

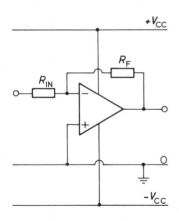

Figure 7.12(a) Dual supply version of voltage-biased amplifier

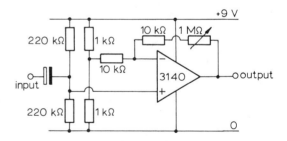

Figure 7.13(a) Opamp non-inverting amplifier

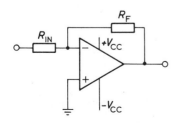

Figure 7.12(b) Simplified circuit diagram

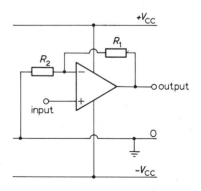

Figure 7.13(b) Dual supply version of non-inverting amplifier

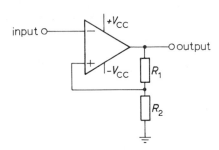

Figure 7.13(c)   Simplified circuit diagram

If you need a single-ended DC non-inverting amplifier, just leave out the coupling capacitor and the two 220 kΩ resistors. A dual-supply version is usually more convenient, however, as the single-ended circuit will reference all its voltages to $V_{CC}/2$.

7.8   Clipping distortion in amplifiers

Refer back to Figure 7.6, and imagine what would happen if the bias voltage was changed. An increase in the bias would result in the flattening or *clipping* of the lower edge of the output. Too small a bias voltage will cause clipping of the upper edge of the output. In either case, reducing the amplitude of the input signal will reduce the clipping. When designing amplifiers it is difficult to get the bias exactly right, but you can see that this does not matter as long as the signal is small. Now imagine that the bias is correct but the amplitude of the input is increased. Now the output signal may hit both earth and the supply, clipping both edges. For very large input the output becomes a square wave.

Whenever clipping takes place, the output wave is not the same shape as the input wave; it has been *distorted*. As, according to Fourier, any wave can be formed by the addition of a number of harmonics, the clipping of a wave results in the addition of harmonics which our ears hear. A distorted wave sounds different; sometimes the distortion may be unpleasant, and sometimes we may think it improves the original sound. The output from an electric guitar is often amplified by an overdriven amplifier called a 'fuzz box' which clips the wave. The effects of incorrectly biasing (two traces) or overdriving (one trace) an amplifier can be seen in the CRO traces of Figure 7.14.

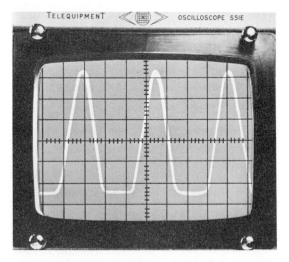

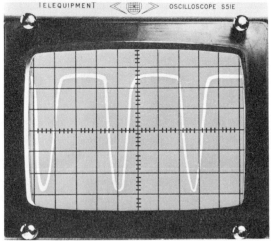

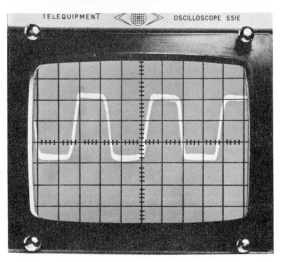

Figure 7.14   Clipping distortion

7.9 Multistage amplifiers

In many practical situations the voltage gain required cannot be provided by any of the amplifiers described. The answer is to join several amplifiers in series, output to input. If the separate amplifier stages are AC amplifiers, each will have its own coupling capacitor and so the stages will be joined by these capacitors. This is called *capacitor coupling*. The total voltage gain of an amplifier consisting of several stages is found by multiplying the gains of the individual stages together:

$$A_v = A_{v1} A_{v2} A_{v3} \text{ etc.}$$

This equation only holds if the rule of ten as described in Section 7.6 is obeyed. To apply this law we will need to know the input and output impedances of the various circuits. These will be considered in Chapter 8, when we attempt to make systems out of circuits.

When the rule of ten works for a pair of coupled circuits, they are said to be *matched*. You have to match the components of a hi-fi system if it is to work satisfactorily.

It is possible to make multistage DC amplifiers by connecting DC amplifier stages together; but beware, as they rarely work as the designer expects.

7.10 Amplifier output stages

Most AC amplifiers end with a loudspeaker, and most DC amplifiers drive an electric motor. In either case the final stage of the amplifier has to provide *power* rather than just *voltage*. The last stage in a multistage amplifier is called the *output*

stage, and so most output stages will be *power amplifiers*.

7.11 Transistor output stages

The obvious starting points are the two transistor drivers of Section 5.7. The common-emitter driver (Figure 5.9) is really an inverter with the transducer in its collector lead. This would not be satisfactory if the transducer was a loudspeaker and the input to the driver was AC. Some kind of bias would be required, and possible circuits are given in Figure 7.15(a). If the emitter-follower driver (Figure 5.10) is connected directly to the previous amplifier stage, it can get its bias from this stage and so no bias resistors or coupling capacitors are required. This is shown in Figure 7.15(b). In both output stages the transistor is in series with the loudspeaker and the same current must flow through each of them. This kind of output stage is known as *class A*. The circuits of Figure 7.15 suffer from a disadvantage that requires some knowledge of the construction of a loudspeaker to understand.

7.12 The loudspeaker

A loudspeaker consists of a coil of wire attached to a cardboard cone which is mounted in such a way that the coil is able to move between the poles of a magnet. When a current is passed through the coil, a force acts on it which tends to move the coil towards or away from the magnet depending on the direction of the current. The size of the force depends on the size of the current, and so the movement of the coil and cone is a copy of the variations in the current. An

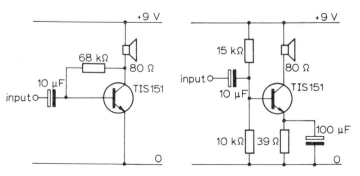

Figure 7.15(a) Common emitter output stage

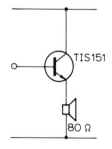

Figure 7.15(b) Emitter follower output stage

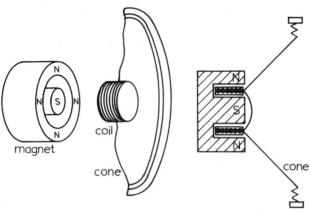

Figure 7.16   Construction of loudspeaker

alternating current with a frequency in the audible range causes the cone to vibrate with the same frequency; as the cone has a large area in contact with the air, sound waves are produced. The loudspeaker is therefore a transducer which converts alternating currents to sound, and the output stage of the amplifier has to generate these alternating currents from the alternating voltages applied to its input. The construction of a loudspeaker is illustrated in Figure 7.16.

Every loudspeaker has an impedance, which mainly consists of the resistance of the coil. They are manufactured in various standard values, 3 Ω, 4 Ω, 8 Ω, 15 Ω, 60 Ω and 80 Ω, of which the small 80 Ω loudspeakers are of the most use in the usual electronic project. If 9 V is applied to a 80 Ω loudspeaker a current of about 100 mA flows, which is just about within the current-carrying

capacity of a BC109. The power dissipated as heat in the loudspeaker will be given by I^2R or $(0.1)^2 \times 80 = 0.8$ W. Most small loudspeakers are rated at 0.3 W, and so it is not good for their health to be connected directly to 9 V. In a correctly biased circuit the output voltage with no input is $\frac{1}{2}V_{CC}$, and so the current will be only 50 mA in the case described and the power only 0.2 W. Once AC is applied to the circuit, the power in the loudspeaker will be reduced. It is therefore safe to use a 80 Ω loudspeaker in a 9 V circuit as shown in this book, provided that the circuit is working correctly.

When experimenting it is a good idea to join a 100 Ω resistor in series with the loudspeaker. This will reduce the loudness of the sound but it will then be impossible to damage the loudspeaker.

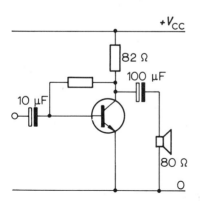

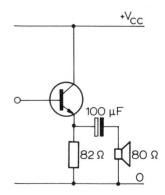

Figure 7.17   Common-emitter (left) and emitter-follower (right) output stages

7.13 Improved class A output stages

In the output stages of Section 7.11 and Figure 7.15 there is a standing current flowing through the loudspeaker even when there is no input signal. This displaces the coil in the magnet, and the loudspeaker is not operating as it was designed. In warning devices and the like this does not matter, but if the loudspeaker has to reproduce speech or music the displacement may produce distortion. Only the AC part of the signal needs to pass through the loudspeaker, and this can flow through a capacitor. Figure 7.17 shows common-emitter and emitter-follower output stages in which the loudspeaker is driven through a coupling capacitor and a resistor is added of resistance equal to the impedance of the loudspeaker. This circuit is still considered as class A.

7.14 An opamp output stage

The main disadvantage of the class A output stage is the standing current which is required to bias the output to $\frac{1}{2}V_{CC}$. If the resistor in series with the transistor is replaced by a transistor, the standing current is no longer required and the output stage becomes class B.

The second transistor is PNP and is connected as shown in Figure 7.18(a). Both transistors are in common-emitter mode, with the NPN transistor conducting during one half of the AC cycle and the PNP transistor conducting during the other half. It is easy to see why this kind of output circuit is also called *push-pull*.

With no AC input both points X and Y are at $\frac{1}{2}V_{CC}$, both transistors are cut off and no standing current flows. When an AC signal is applied to the input, the output will follow it in the normal manner of the emitter follower. Now comes the problem. The output is always 0.7 V behind the input, which means that a section of the input 1.4 V wide is lost. The effect can be seen in the graphs of Figure 7.18(b).

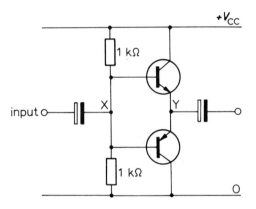

7.18(a) Class B output stage

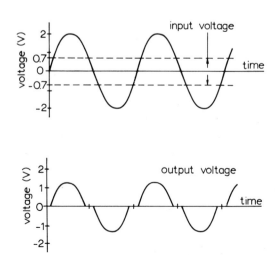

Figure 7.18(b) Input and output for class B output stage

This kind of distortion is called *cross-over distortion*. This is a particularly serious kind of distortion, because the less the amplitude of the signal the greater the distortion, until for amplitudes less than 0.7 V there is no output at all.

The distortion can be removed by the addition of an opamp as in Figure 7.18(c). The circuit is very similar to the opamp buffer circuit, but the feedback is taken from the emitters of the transistors rather than from the output of the opamp. As long as the transistors are operating, the circuit acts like the buffer with 100% negative feedback, giving it unity gain. During the 1.4 V region, when the transistors are turned off, there is no feedback so the opamp has its open-loop gain. The voltage band lost out of the input signal is therefore about 100 000 times smaller, so reducing it to negligible proportions.

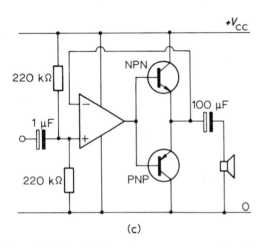

(c)

Figure 7.18(c)   Addition of opamp to remove distortion in class B output stage

The circuit as a whole has an input impedance of 100 kΩ, a voltage gain of 1, but considerable current and power gain. The output current is limited by the current-carrying capacity of the output transistors. Matched pairs of NPN and PNP transistors have been developed for use with class B output stages. Many are Darlingtons, so that their base currents can be supplied by the opamp without overloading it. Good examples are the TIP 121 (NPN) and the TIP 126 (PNP), which can carry up to 5 A and have a minimum h_{FE} of 1000.

The circuit of Figure 7.18(c) is intended for driving loudspeakers and has an output coupling capacitor. Class B output stages can be used without the capacitor for driving electric motors. The input would then be a DC voltage, and the 1 μF capacitor and the two 220 kΩ resistors could also be omitted.

7.15   Volume control

Most audio amplifiers need some way of adjusting the loudness of the output. This can be done by varying the voltage gain of one of the stages, but a more usual solution is to use a potentiometer wired as an AC potential divider (Figure 7.19). The circuit will work without the coupling capacitors, but then a standing current flows through the potentiometer which can give rise to unwanted noise.

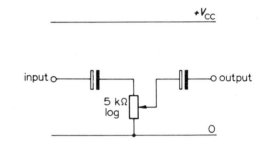

Figure 7.19   AC potential divider as volume control

The ear does not hear loudness on a linear scale. That is, when the energy in a sound is doubled, it sounds to us much less than twice as loud. Special potentiometers called *logarithmic* potentiometers are manufactured which have non-linear tracks, so that equal turns of the knob appear to us to increase the output by equal amounts.

7.16   The summing amplifier or mixer

This circuit is a special case of the inverting opamp amplifier. It can be used in a DC form to add voltages together, or it can be provided with coupling capacitors and used to combine AC signals as a mixer. Either form can use single or dual power supplies. When using it in its single-ended DC form, remember that the input voltages are measured relative to the reference voltage at the non-inverting input, which is usually $\frac{1}{2}V_{CC}$. On a 9 V supply this means that inputs of 6 V and 2.5 V would be taken as + 1.5 V

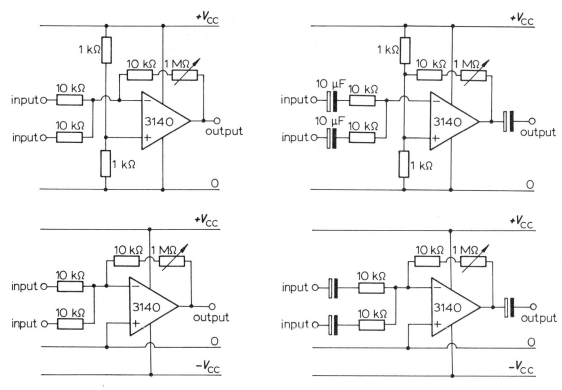

Figure 7.20   Summer or mixer circuits

and −2 V, giving an input of −0.5 V. If the gain of the amplifier was set to 5, this would give an output of +2.5 V relative to $\frac{1}{2}V_{CC}$ and so a real output voltage of 7 V. You can see why DC summers are usually powered by a dual supply where all voltages are relative to zero. All four forms of the circuit are illustrated in Figure 7.20. The number of inputs is not limited to two.

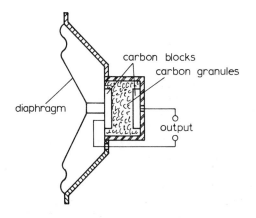

Figure 7.21(a)   Carbon microphone

7.17   AC input transducers

When an amplifier is on test, the input will usually come from a signal generator. However, real systems must be driven from some kind of input transducer. For AC amplifiers these will be microphones, record player pickups and tape heads. In this section we will spend some time looking at some of the transducers you are likely to use, and in particular how they can be connected to your systems. The *carbon microphone* consists of a mass of loosely packed carbon granules between two carbon plates, the whole acting as a resistor (Figure 7.21(a)). One of the carbon blocks is attached to a light aluminium diaphragm, and when sound waves reach it the diaphragm and the block are forced to vibrate. During the vibrations the carbon granules are forced together and moved apart. The resistance of the microphone depends on the area of the granules in contact, so that the resistance falls when they are forced together and rises when they move apart.

The alternating variations in pressure in the sound wave are therefore converted into variations in resistance. There are two ways in which the resistance variations can be converted to alternating voltages. The microphone can be made part of a potential divider, as shown in Figure 7.21(b), or the microphone can be connected in series with the primary coil of a step-up transformer. Using the second method it is possible to obtain an output voltage of sufficient amplitude to drive an output transducer without an amplifier.

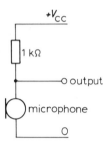

Figure 7.21(b)   Microphone circuit

The carbon microphone is used in the *telephone handset*. The handset also contains an output transducer, the *telephone earpiece*. The construction of this device does not really belong in this section, as it is an output rather than an input transducer. It will, however, work in both directions, acting as a microphone as well as a loudspeaker. Figure 7.21(c) shows an earphone contains an unusual magnet. It is made up of a small permanent magnet and two soft iron pole pieces. Coils of wire are wrapped round the iron. When an alternating current is passed through the coils, a magnetic field is produced in the iron which sometimes opposes and sometimes helps the field of the permanent magnet. The result is a magnetic field which is always in the same direction but varies in strength at the frequency of the alternating current. In other words, the permanent magnet gives a kind of magnetic bias. In front of the magnet is a diaphragm made of magnetic alloy which is attracted by the magnet and so also vibrates at the frequency of the alternating current, generating sound waves in the air. If the device is used as a microphone the incoming sound waves make the diaphragm vibrate, which varies the strength of the magnetic field and so induces an alternating voltage across the coils.

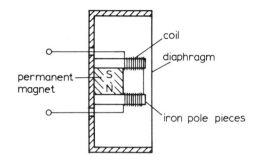

Figure 7.21(c)   Earphone

The *moving-coil microphone* (Figure 7.22) is very similar in construction to a moving-coil loudspeaker. In fact a loudspeaker can act as a microphone, the miniature $80\,\Omega$ type being particularly useful. When sound waves cause the cone or diaphragm to vibrate, the coil is forced to move through the magnetic field and therefore has an alternating voltage induced across it.

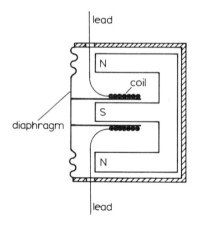

Figure 7.22   Moving-coil microphone

The *crystal microphone* is shown in Figure 7.23. When a crystal of Rochelle salt is compressed the crystal generates a voltage across it. To make a microphone the crystal is held between two metal plates and one side is mechanically connected to a diaphragm.

The better and more expensive *record player pick-up cartridges* (Figure 7.24) are moving coil. Those in cheaper equipment are *ceramic*, which work in a manner similar to that of the crystal microphone.

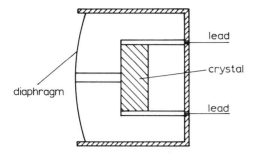

Figure 7.23 Crystal microphone

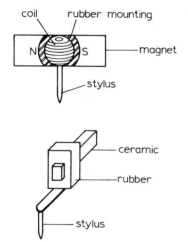

Figure 7.24 Moving-coil pick-up cartridge

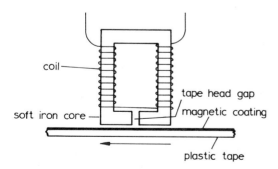

Figure 7.25 Magnetic tape head

The *tape head* is shown in Figure 7.25. The tape used in a tape recorder is made of plastic with a coating of a material that can be magnetized. As magnetized areas on the tape pass under the tape head gap, a magnetic field is formed in the soft iron core. The variations in this field induce voltages across the coil.

7.18 Pre-amplifier circuits

A pre-amplifier is a circuit that joins an input transducer to the main amplifier. It has three functions. It must raise the voltage amplitude of the signal from the transducer to the value required by the main amplifier. It must have an input impedance that will not load the transducer and an output impedance that will not be loaded by the main amplifier (it matches the transducer to the main amplifier). It must correct any frequency abnormalities in the signal from the transducer. The last is beyond an elementary book, but we can look again at the transducers of the previous section and consider what kind of pre-amplifier they require in the light of the first two conditions.

The carbon microphone has a typical resistance of 1 kΩ and, when connected in series with a 1 kΩ resistor, forms a potential divider giving a peak AC output of up to 1 V for normal speech. No pre-amplifier is required as long as the main amplifier has an input impedance of 10 kΩ or more, and clipping will be a problem unless the gain of the amplifier is very low.

The crystal-microphone and ceramic pick-up give a large output of up to 100 mV but they have a very high impedance. The main property of the pre-amplifier is to have a high input impedance and low output impedance. The obvious choice is the opamp AC non-inverting amplifier.

The rest of the transducers mentioned give output voltages in the range 1 to 5 mA and have low impedance. Any of the voltage amplifiers described in the section would prove satisfactory.

The best way is always to connect the transducer to a CRO and measure the output voltage.

7.19 Filters

Filters are circuits that allow AC of some frequencies to pass through them more easily than others. A complete study of the subject would take a large volume in itself, and here there is only space for a consideration of the two most simple.

Consider the circuit of Figure 7.26. It is a potential divider with a capacitor as the upper half. The reactance (AC resistance) of a capacitor goes down as the frequency increases, so at low frequencies the reactance will be high and the output low while at high frequencies the reactance will be low and the output high. The circuit allows high frequencies to pass more easily than low frequencies. It is called a *high-pass filter*.

The filter shown in Figure 7.27 is the other way round and will pass low frequencies better than high; it is a *low-pass filter*.

In either case the output will be half the input at a frequency given by

$$f = \frac{1}{2\pi RC}$$

where R is in ohms and C is in farads.

A filter changes not only the amplitude of an AC voltage but also its *phase*. Three high-pass filters in series will change the phase of one particular frequency by 180°. This means that at that frequency the signal is inverted. The amplitude of the signal is reduced by a factor of 29. Figure 7.28 shows such a filter connected to the input of a variable-gain inverting amplifier with the output fed back to the input. The amplifier has positive feedback at one frequency only, the frequency that gives a 180° phase shift. If the gain of the amplifier is set to just above 29, the circuit will oscillate with a sine-wave output of frequency

$$f = \frac{1}{15RC}$$

The circuit is known as a *phase-shift oscillator*.

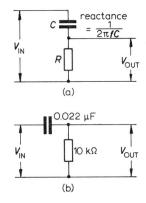

$V_{OUT} = \frac{1}{2}V_{IN}$
when
$R = \frac{1}{2\pi fC}$ at break frequency

$V_{OUT} \ll V_{IN}$
when
$R \ll \frac{1}{2\pi fC}$ at low frequencies

Figure 7.26　High-pass filter

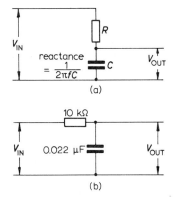

$V_{OUT} = \frac{1}{2}V_{IN}$
when
$R = \frac{1}{2\pi fC}$ at break frequency

$V_{OUT} \ll V_{IN}$
when
$\frac{1}{2\pi fC} \ll R$ at high frequencies

Figure 7.27　Low-pass filter

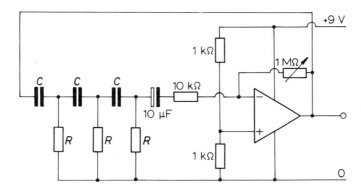

Figure 7.28 Phase-shift oscillator

7.20 The rectifier unit or diode pump

The purpose of this circuit is to generate a DC voltage which is proportional to the amplitude of the AC signal applied to the input. The AC signal will usually come from the output of an amplifier and contain a DC bias, which must first be removed by a coupling capacitor. The next stage is to half-wave rectify the signal by two diodes. Lastly the signal is smoothed by a capacitor. A resistor in parallel to the capacitor allows the capacitor to discharge when the amplitude of the input signal falls. The whole process is illustrated by graphs in Figure 7.29.

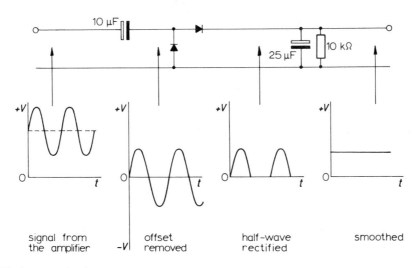

Figure 7.29 Diode pump circuit

Summary

Amplifier basics

The AC amplifier has

AC voltage gain $A_v = \dfrac{\text{change in output voltage}}{\text{change in input voltage}}$

$= \dfrac{v_{OUT}}{v_{IN}}$

AC current gain $A_i = \dfrac{\text{change in output current}}{\text{change in input current}}$

$= \dfrac{i_{OUT}}{i_{IN}}$

AC power gain $G_p = \dfrac{\text{AC power out}}{\text{AC power in}}$

$G_p = A_v A_i$

AC voltage, current or power can be peak or RMS. For a sine wave only,

$$\text{RMS current} = \dfrac{\text{peak current}}{\sqrt{2}}$$

$$\text{RMS voltage} = \dfrac{\text{peak voltage}}{\sqrt{2}}$$

RMS voltage × RMS current = RMS power

peak voltage × peak current = peak power

The input impedance of an amplifier is its effective resistance to an AC input and is equal to the ratio of its input voltage to its input current:

$$r_{IN} = \dfrac{v_{IN}}{i_{IN}}$$

The output resistance of an amplifier is the internal resistance that the amplifier offers to an AC signal taken from its output. It is the ratio of the output voltage to output current when the amplifier is delivering maximum power.

The common-emitter amplifier

The emitter terminal is common to the input and output circuits. The input is to the base, the output is from the collector.

$$r_{IN} = \dfrac{0.025 h_{FE}}{I_C} \qquad A_i = h_{FE}$$

$$A_v = \dfrac{R_C I_C}{0.025} \ (I_C \text{ in mA, } R_C \text{ in k}\Omega)$$

If the amplifier is biased with output at $V_{CC}/2$, then $A_v = 20\,V_{CC}$.

$$r_{OUT} = R_C \qquad G_p = \dfrac{h_{FE} R_C I_C}{0.025}$$

The amplifier is inverting.

The common-collector or emitter-follower amplifier

The input is to the base, the output is from the emitter.

$$r_{IN} = h_{FE} R_E \qquad r_{OUT} = R_E$$

R_E is the emitter resistor and load in parallel.

$$A_v = 1 \qquad A_i = h_{FE} \qquad G_p = h_{FE}$$

Mainly used as a buffer amplifier.
The amplifier is non-inverting.

Feedback

Negative, DC: Used to give stable bias conditions.
Negative, AC: Reduces A_v and improves quality in amplifiers.
Positive, DC: Gives fast switch in bistable and Schmitt Triggers.
Positive, AC: Produces oscillation in amplifiers.

Basic circuits

Inverting current-biased AC amplifier

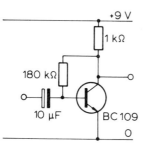

Fixed voltage gain of about 150. Current gain equal to h_{FE} of the transistor.

Inverting voltage-biased AC amplifier

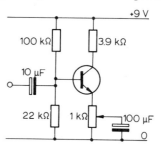

Voltage gain variable between 4 and 150 by potentiometer. Current gain equal to the h_{FE} of the transistor.

Inverting AC/DC amplifier summer/mixer

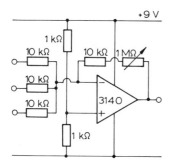

Voltage gain variable between 1 and 100 by potentiometer. Three inputs shown. Coupling capacitors required for AC use.

Non-inverting AC/DC amplifier

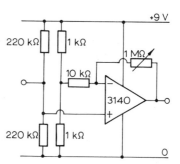

Voltage gain variable between 1 and 100 by potentiometer. Coupling capacitors required for AC use.

Class B transducer driver/output stage

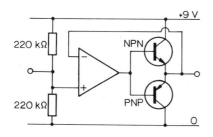

Unity voltage gain. Use with coupling capacitors on input and output for AC

Voltage divider/volume control

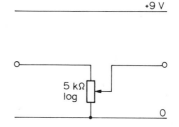

Use with coupling capacitors on input and output for AC.

Coupling capacitor

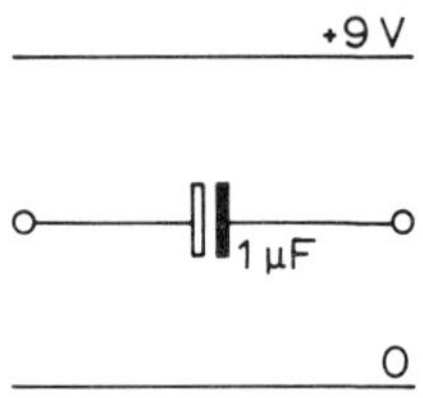

+9 V

1 µF

0

Suitable for coupling AC to high-impedance inputs.

Coupling capacitor

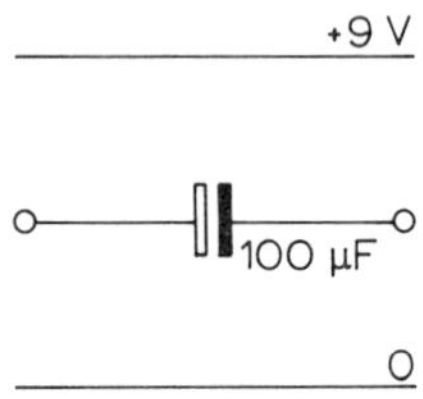

+9 V

100 µF

0

Suitable for coupling AC to loudspeakers.

Coupling capacitor

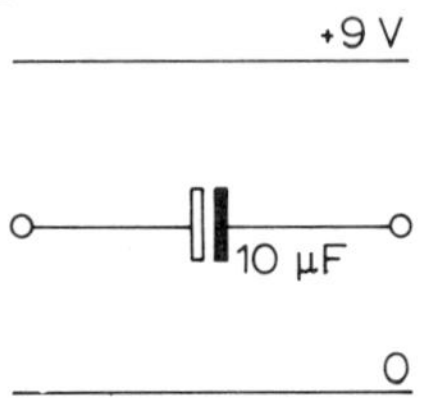

+9 V

10 µF

0

Suitable for coupling AC to medium-impedance inputs.

High-pass filter

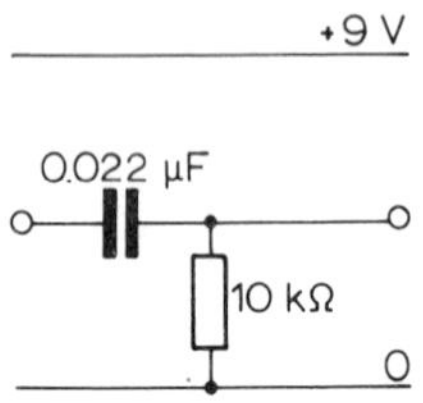

+9 V

0.022 µF

10 kΩ

0

Amplitude of AC input reduced to half at 750 Hz.

Low-pass filter

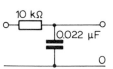

+9 V

10 kΩ

0.022 µF

0

Amplitude of AC input reduced to half at 750 Hz.

Rectifier unit

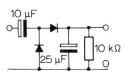

+9 V

10 µF

25 µF

10 kΩ

0

AC amplitude converted to DC voltage level.

Carbon microphone

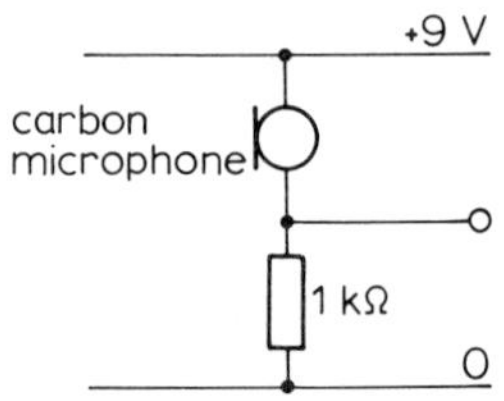

+9 V

carbon microphone

1 kΩ

0

Audio input transducer. Converts sound to an alternating voltage.

Crystal microphone

+9 V

crystal microphone

0

Audio input transducer. Converts sound to an alternating voltage.

Phase-shift oscillator

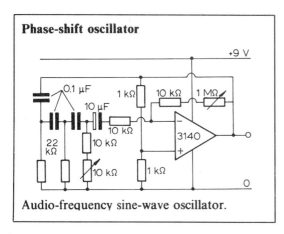

Audio-frequency sine-wave oscillator.

Moving-coil microphone

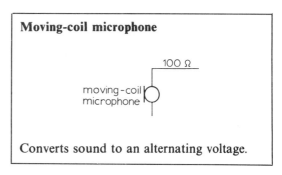

Converts sound to an alternating voltage.

Questions

1 Find the peak-to-peak, peak, and RMS voltages of the signal from the cathode ray oscilloscope traces shown. The Y-amplifier is set to 500 mV/cm. Zero volts is in the centre of the screen.

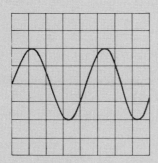

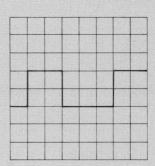

2 A sine-wave voltage of 25 mV peak-to-peak was connected to the input of an amplifier. The output, when displayed on a CRO, looked like the diagram shown. Deduce as much as you can about the signal and the amplifier.

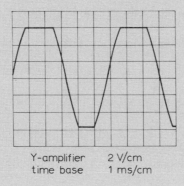

Y-amplifier   2 V/cm
time base   1 ms/cm

3 The input and output signals from a voltage amplifier are connected to the two channels of a dual-trace CRO. The output is the upper trace with its Y-amplifier set to 2 V/cm, and the input is the lower with its Y-amplifier set to 50 mV/cm. The value of the time base setting is shown below each diagram.

   Deduce from the CRO traces the voltage gain at each frequency, and display your answers as a table with columns for gain and frequency.

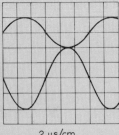

2 μs/cm

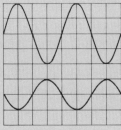

2.5 ms/cm

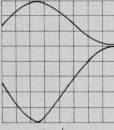

3 μs/cm

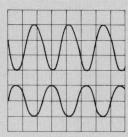

3.5 ms/cm

What other information can you deduce about the amplifier?

4 Two amplifier stages of voltage gains 50 and 24 are joined in series by a coupling capacitor. Explain why a coupling capacitor is necessary. If the two stages are perfectly matched, what will be the voltage gain of the resulting two-stage amplifier?

   What do you understand by the term 'perfectly matched'?

5 The diagram shows two current-biased amplifiers. Which one has the better bias method, and which one will have the larger voltage gain? Explain your answers.

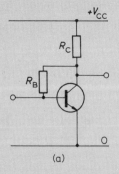

(a)

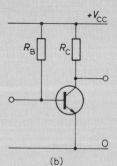

(b)

6 What is the purpose of a decoupling capacitor in a voltage-biased transistor amplifier, and how does it alter the gain of the amplifier?

7 Design an inverting opamp amplifier with a voltage gain of 20 and an input resistor of 10 kΩ. How would you alter your amplifier so that it would only amplify AC inputs?

8 Design a non-inverting opamp amplifier with a voltage gain of 10. Draw both single-ended and dual-power-supply versions of your circuit.

9 Sketch the input/output voltage characteristic for a transistor connected in common-emitter mode as an inverter. Use this graph to explain the following:

(a) A common-emitter amplifier inverts the signal.
(b) A high-gain amplifier can be used to convert a sine wave to a square wave.
(c) Correct bias is less important in the early stages of an amplifier than it is in the output stage.

10 When two sine waves of nearly equal frequency are mixed together the amplitude of the resultant wave varies at a frequency called the beat frequency. The system shown was designed to illustrate this. Describe the part played by each basic circuit in the complete system.

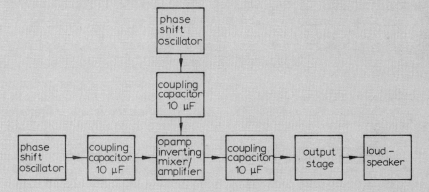

11 The system shown is designed for use in a library. Describe the action of the complete system and the part played in it by each basic circuit.

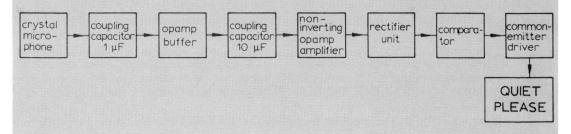

Systems from basic circuits

8.1 Designing systems

The first step in designing a system is to make up your mind exactly what the system is required to do. It should now be obvious which input and output transducers will be used, and these will lead to the selection of the input and output units. In some very simple systems it will now be possible to find a basic circuit which performs the processing required by itself, but more usually the processing will have to be performed by joining several basic circuits together.

Choosing the best combination to perform a particular task is a skill that is well worth developing. Usually several combinations of circuits will work, but some will be better than others because of superior performance or lower cost. Sometimes you will have to choose between performance and cost. Figure 8.1 consists of a number of boxes, one for each of the basic circuits, most having input and output but some with input or output only. The input of each circuit is on the left and is marked with the input resistance or impedance in brackets. The output impedance is in brackets on the right. Below each circuit diagram is a summary of the processing function of the circuit.

At the top right-hand corner of each circuit is the number of the chapter where additional information about it can be found. You should copy these boxes and cut them out so that they can be arranged in any order. You should be able to select the circuits you need for your system.

Now comes the important checking stage. Start with an input transducer and imagine it in one extreme state. Work your way through the system using the function summaries to decide the state of each output in turn until you find the state of the output transducer. Is this what you want? If not, modify your system until it is. Now imagine the input transducer in the opposite extreme state and work through your system again. Has the output transducer changed its state? Lastly, imagine the input transducer changing from one extreme to the other and check again that the system is what you require. Draw the final system as a series of boxes with just the title of the basic circuit inside.

The procedure described above works best for systems concerned with switching. If the system involves amplifiers a slightly different procedure is required. First of all imagine the system with no AC input, and then with the input applied. In systems involving amplification and switching you should check that the output transducer is in the required state with no input signal. With multistage amplifiers check that you have enough voltage gain to obtain an output voltage swing of close to the power supplies, but not so much gain that clipping occurs. In particular, in AC amplifiers check that coupling capacitors have been added where required.

While you are checking the system you will no doubt think of alternative systems that would achieve the same result. Build these systems out of your boxes and check them through as before.

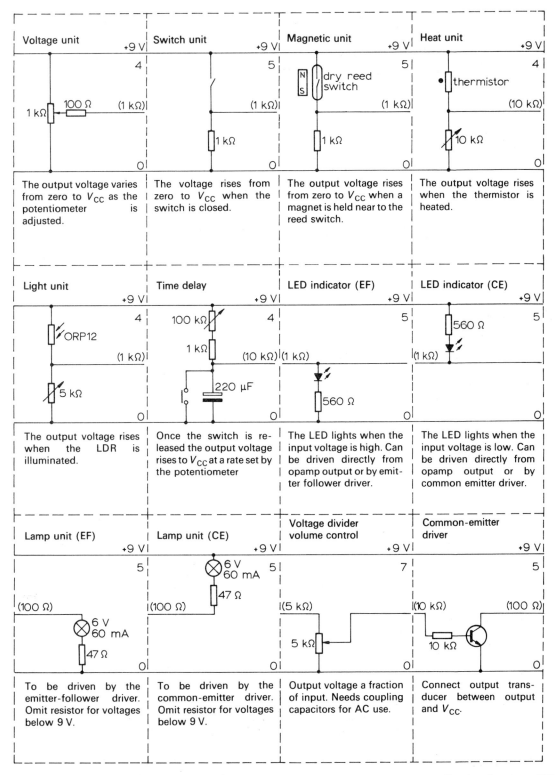

The output voltage varies from zero to V_{CC} as the potentiometer is adjusted.

The voltage rises from zero to V_{CC} when the switch is closed.

The output voltage rises from zero to V_{CC} when a magnet is held near to the reed switch.

The output voltage rises when the thermistor is heated.

The output voltage rises when the LDR is illuminated.

Once the switch is released the output voltage rises to V_{CC} at a rate set by the potentiometer

The LED lights when the input voltage is high. Can be driven directly from opamp output or by emitter follower driver.

The LED lights when the input voltage is low. Can be driven directly from opamp output or by common emitter driver.

To be driven by the emitter-follower driver. Omit resistor for voltages below 9 V.

To be driven by the common-emitter driver. Omit resistor for voltages below 9 V.

Output voltage a fraction of input. Needs coupling capacitors for AC use.

Connect output transducer between output and V_{CC}.

Figure 8.1

Continued on page 130

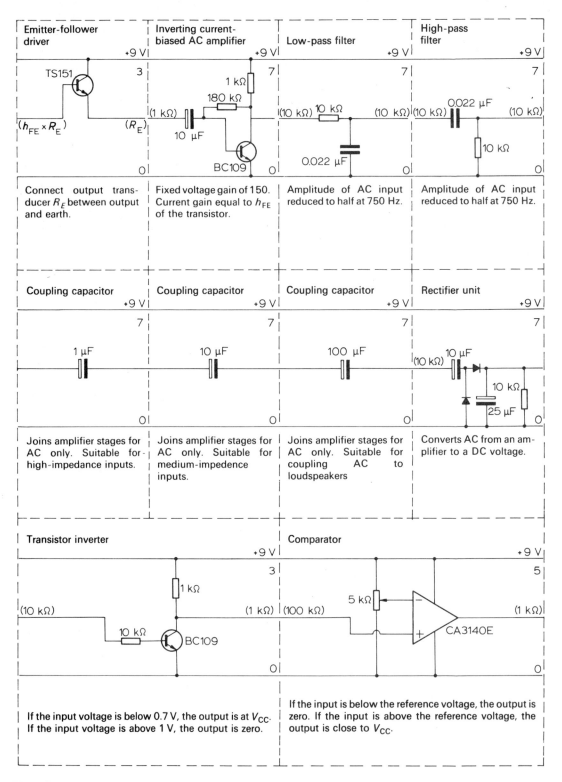

Figure 8.1   (continued)

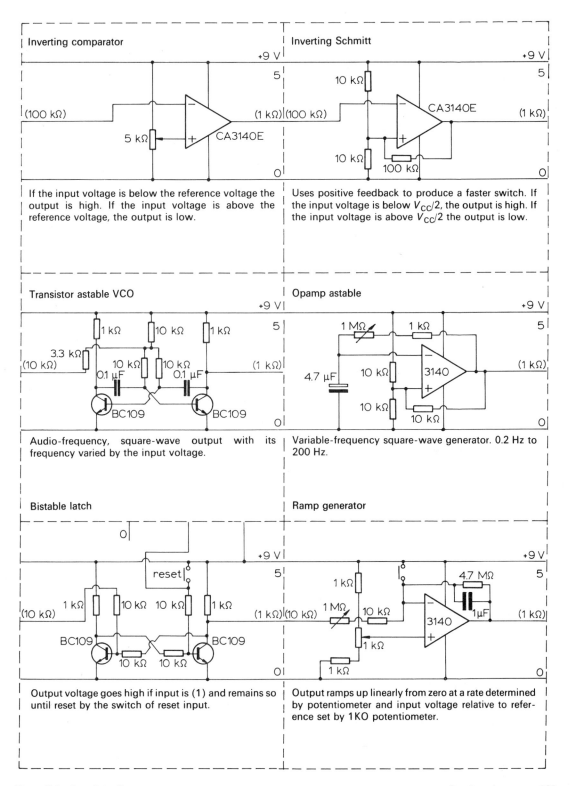

Inverting comparator

If the input voltage is below the reference voltage the output is high. If the input voltage is above the reference voltage, the output is low.

Inverting Schmitt

Uses positive feedback to produce a faster switch. If the input voltage is below $V_{CC}/2$, the output is high. If the input voltage is above $V_{CC}/2$ the output is low.

Transistor astable VCO

Audio-frequency, square-wave output with its frequency varied by the input voltage.

Opamp astable

Variable-frequency square-wave generator. 0.2 Hz to 200 Hz.

Bistable latch

Output voltage goes high if input is (1) and remains so until reset by the switch of reset input.

Ramp generator

Output ramps up linearly from zero at a rate determined by potentiometer and input voltage relative to reference set by 1KO potentiometer.

Figure 8.1 (continued)

Continued on page 132

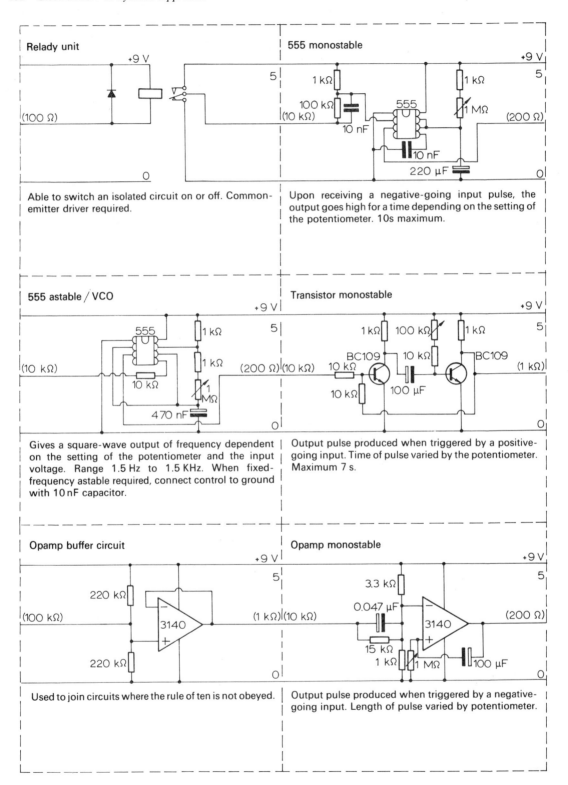

Relady unit

Able to switch an isolated circuit on or off. Common-emitter driver required.

555 monostable

Upon receiving a negative-going input pulse, the output goes high for a time depending on the setting of the potentiometer. 10s maximum.

555 astable / VCO

Gives a square-wave output of frequency dependent on the setting of the potentiometer and the input voltage. Range 1.5 Hz to 1.5 KHz. When fixed-frequency astable required, connect control to ground with 10 nF capacitor.

Transistor monostable

Output pulse produced when triggered by a positive-going input. Time of pulse varied by the potentiometer. Maximum 7 s.

Opamp buffer circuit

Used to join circuits where the rule of ten is not obeyed.

Opamp monostable

Output pulse produced when triggered by a negative-going input. Length of pulse varied by potentiometer.

Figure 8.1   (continued)

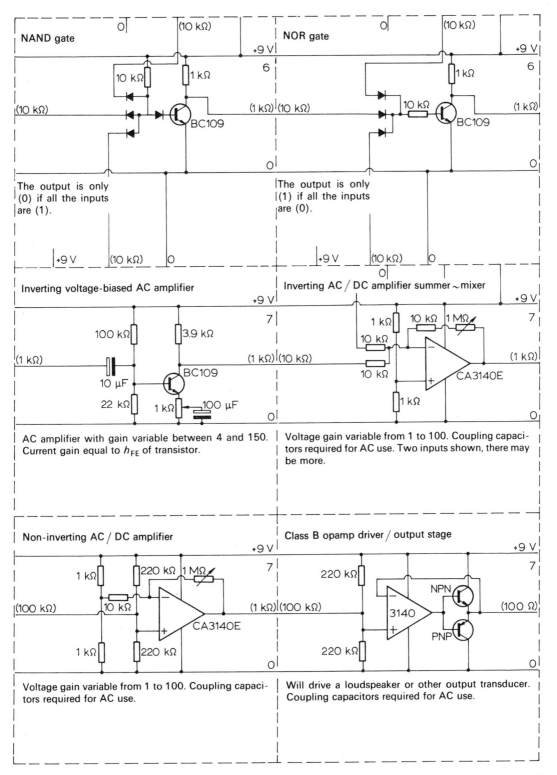

NAND gate

The output is only (0) if all the inputs are (1).

NOR gate

The output is only (1) if all the inputs are (0).

Inverting voltage-biased AC amplifier

AC amplifier with gain variable between 4 and 150. Current gain equal to h_{FE} of transistor.

Inverting AC / DC amplifier summer ~ mixer

Voltage gain variable from 1 to 100. Coupling capacitors required for AC use. Two inputs shown, there may be more.

Non-inverting AC / DC amplifier

Voltage gain variable from 1 to 100. Coupling capacitors required for AC use.

Class B opamp driver / output stage

Will drive a loudspeaker or other output transducer. Coupling capacitors required for AC use.

Figure 8.1 (continued)

Continued on page 134

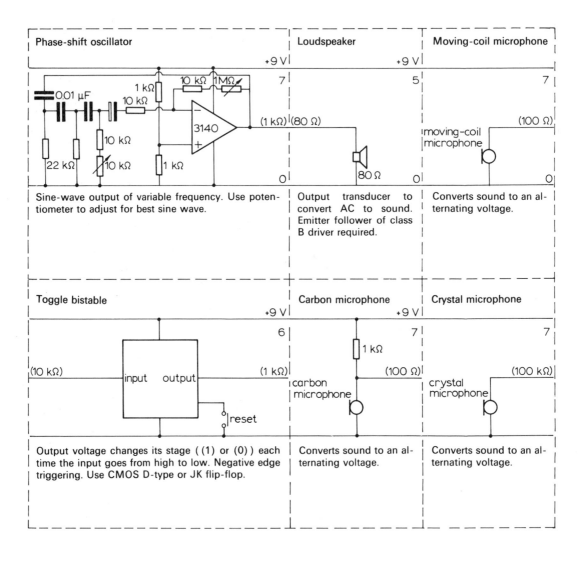

Phase-shift oscillator	Loudspeaker	Moving-coil microphone
Sine-wave output of variable frequency. Use potentiometer to adjust for best sine wave.	Output transducer to convert AC to sound. Emitter follower of class B driver required.	Converts sound to an alternating voltage.
Toggle bistable	Carbon microphone	Crystal microphone
Output voltage changes its stage ((1) or (0)) each time the input goes from high to low. Negative edge triggering. Use CMOS D-type or JK flip-flop.	Converts sound to an alternating voltage.	Converts sound to an alternating voltage.

Figure 8.1   (continued)

8.2 Impedance matching

Impedance matching is the name given to checking that the input and output resistances or impedances of successive circuits obey the rule of ten. Go through each system that you have designed and make sure that for each pair of boxes joined together the output impedance/resistance of the first is at least ten times smaller than the input impedance/resistance of the second. Sometimes this can only be achieved by substituting some basic circuits in your system for others with the same function. Sometimes a buffer circuit such as the emitter-follower driver or the opamp buffer must be inserted between two basic circuits whose output and input impedances do not match. Sometimes perfect matching is impossible and the system will still work but with reduced performance.

You may wonder how the values for the input and output impedances of the various basic circuits are calculated. For a great many of the circuits the values are obvious. The inverter and all the circuits derived from it use a 10 kΩ input resistor; all input currents have to flow through this, giving the circuit an input resistance of 10 kΩ. In the same way the output current flows through the collector resistor, giving an output impedance of 1 kΩ.

The output impedances of the transducer units are difficult to calculate because they vary as the resistance of the transducer changes and the potentiometer is adjusted. For these and many of the other circuits a value has been given that has been found to work in practice.

Example *Consider the impedance matching of the system shown below.*

At each junction between basic circuits we must multiply the output impedance by ten and check that it is equal to or less than the following input impedance.

Consider the junction between the light unit and the comparator. The output impedance is 1 kΩ. Multiplied by ten, this becomes 10 kΩ. The next input impedance is 100 kΩ, which is better than required. At the next junction the output impedance is 1 kΩ once more, so needing at least 10 kΩ input impedance to follow. The 555 circuit has this impedance, so that once more the rule of ten is obeyed and the circuits match. Check the next junction and you will see that this is a good match. The last junction is 100 Ω into 100 Ω and appears to be a poor match. This, however, is the special case of a driver and a transducer where power transfer is more important than loading, and equal input and output impedances give the maximum power transfer.

8.3 Circuit production and evaluation

The rather grand title of this section describes a simple procedure.

Look up the circuit for each box and convert the boxes into circuits. So much for the circuit production.

Now for the evaluation. Look through the various alternative circuits you have produced and decide upon the best. A transistor costs about half as much as an opamp, and a 555 timer costs a little more than an opamp. The fewer components there are in your circuit, the fewer soldering errors you are likely to make. Transistor circuits can be spaced out more and so are easier to solder than those involving ICs. Input and output transducers are usually the most expensive part of any system.

The only real test of any system is to build it and see if it works. You could be very foolhardy and solder up the circuit at once on some kind of circuit board as described in later sections in this chapter, or you could use some kind of tem-

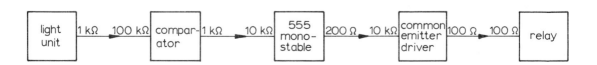

porary circuit system. The ideal system would be a number of circuit boards, each containing a basic circuit, that could be plugged together in any order just like the boxes of Section 8.1. If you were going to design a lot of systems it might be worth building a set (they can be bought from Electrolern, whose address is given at the front of the book).

The alternative to a set of basic circuit modules is some form of *breadboard*. In electronics a breadboard is a small flat plastic box with lines of holes in the top (see Figure 8.2). Below the rows of holes are metal contacts, so that if one lead wire of a number of components is pushed into each of the holes in a row the leads are connected together. The rows are usually four or five holes long and are marked on the top of the breadboard by a raised strip. Figure 8.2 shows the empty breadboard, the breadboard opened to see the contacts, and a transistor astable built on the breadboard. You will notice the main disadvantage of a breadboard; the circuit looks nothing like the circuit diagram. The advantage is that the circuit can easily be modified, and at the end you can remove the components for future use.

Whatever system you use, *never build the whole system and expect it to work*. It never does. Start with the input transducer unit and connect a voltmeter between the output of this unit and the zero line. Vary the transducer and see that the voltmeter shows the correct change. Most input units contain a variable resistor. Adjust this so that the voltage range is suitable for the next basic circuit. Beware of having the potentiometer set to nothing so that the output voltage is always zero.

If the first unit works, build on the next and move the positive lead of the voltmeter across to its output. Once again vary the transducer and check that the output varies correctly. You may now have two resistors to adjust, so do so thoughtfully and not at random. Slowly build up the system stage by stage until you come to the output transducer. You are now sure to have a working system.

Systems involving amplifiers require the same kind of approach, but a CRO is more useful than a voltmeter. Start with the source of the AC input connected directly to the *Y*-input of the CRO and with the CRO set to DC. Provided that you started with the trace along the centre line of the screen, you will now be able to measure the amplitude of the input and see if it has a DC offset. If the source of AC is a microphone, a

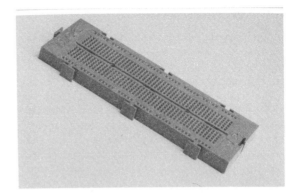

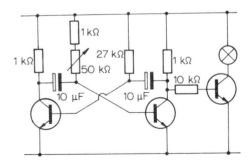

Figure 8.2 Breadboard astable constructed on breadboard and the astable circuit diagram

record player pick-up or a tape unit, you will not be able to obtain a stable graph on the screen because the signal does not continuously repeat itself. Build the first stage to see that there are no loading problems and then replace the source of AC input by a signal generator set to the same amplitude and a frequency of about 1 kHz. You can now build up the system stage by stage, testing as you go. Look out for clipping and stages with little gain. Do not be tempted to turn up the amplitude of the signal generator or CRO, but instead look for the fault in the circuit. If you are looking for a fault in a circuit, first read Section 8.15.

Once the system is completed and working it must be compared with the original specification of what it should do and modified accordingly. Sometimes it is now obvious that the original specification was not practical, and the only course is to alter the specification to fit the system.

8.4   Choice of supply voltages

The basic circuits have all been designed for a supply voltage of 9 V. This is because a variety of 9 V dry cell batteries are available. The circuits will work on a range of supply voltages from 5 V to 12 V and so you are free to choose the most convenient. If the final device is to be fitted into a motor car then you would be sensible to choose 12 V. Any lamps or relays used would have to be rated at this voltage.

Many systems will involve enough logic gates and counters to make it necessary to use one of the logic families. If you choose the 74 series then it has to be 5 V, but CMOS will allow you to retain your 5 to 12 V range. Section 8.5 explains how to join either of the logic families to basic circuits.

8.5   Interfacing the 74 series and CMOS

These two logic families give us a whole new range of basic circuits which we can use in our systems. The problems are:

- When to use logic ICs
- Which type to choose

- How to join them to other basic circuits.

There are some systems where only logic ICs can provide a practical solution. These include any system involving a counter or decoder, and so if you want a seven-segment digital display you must use ICs. In general, if you need to use more than three logic gates in your system, then an IC will give the most convenient solution.

The main advantage of the TTL 74 series is its speed of operation. In most applications it is far faster than necessary, and its main advantage to us is that unused inputs behave as if connected to V_{CC} and can be ignored. This means that if we use a quadruple NAND with four gates on the chip and only require three of them, we can just ignore the fourth. In the same way we can use a three-input NAND as a two-input NAND by just not connecting to the other input. The great disadvantages of this series are its rigid power supply requirements and its power consumption. The power supply must be 5 V, and in addition must be protected against 'spikes' which can be taken as (1)s. This means a regulated power supply capable of supplying about 25 mA per chip used. Batteries are unsuitable and the power supply often costs more than the rest of the system.

CMOS gates use very little power and tolerate variations in supply voltage. They can therefore be run from a 9 V battery or a simple power supply. Their disadvantage lies in their high input impedance which allows inputs to pick up static charges and go to either (1) or (0) at random. In fact the charges picked up from the constructor can be big enough to kill the chip. Diodes inside the chip protect it once the power supply is connected, so you should always handle a CMOS IC by its plastic case and solder its power leads first. Once in the circuit the inputs required will be connected high or low by the rest of the circuit, but unused inputs will be free to pick up charges. This must be prevented by connecting all unused inputs to either of the supply rails. The positive supply rail is usually the most convenient.

Either TTL or CMOS can be driven from the outputs of the basic circuits, but if you want to drive a basic circuit from the output of an IC you may need a driver circuit between them to act as a buffer, particularly in the case of CMOS.

You will see from the above that CMOS is the better choice in most situations.

8.6   The design of a burglar alarm

In this section we will go through the procedure outlined in previous sections on a specific example.

Specification

Each house window and door is to be fitted with a reed switch and magnet so that when opened the switch breaks the circuit. A secondary system will consist of a light beam which will trigger the alarm if broken. The alarm is to consist of a regularly interrupted tone. The circuits are to be battery powered. The system is to be reset by a key switch which will also turn the alarm off.

The input transducers will be reed switches and an LDR. All the reed switches will be connected in series and can be represented by one. The input basic circuits will therefore be the magnetic unit and the light unit. The output transducer will be a loudspeaker.

We can now start to put some basic units together. The alarm should trigger if either the reed opens OR the light beam is broken. The system will contain the OR function, which we can obtain by inverting a NOR gate. If the burglar shuts the door again once the alarm sounds, we do not want it to stop. This means that the system must have some memory. The bistable unit can be included. Figure 8.3 shows the system so far. The intention is that when the system is triggered by either transducer the output of the bistable will go to logical (1) and remain at this until a (1) is applied to the reset input.

Now for the output part of the system. If there is to be a audible warning then an oscillator will

be required that can produce a wave at audio frequency. Let us choose the 555 astable set to about 1 kHz. Another gate will be required to block the output from the astable when the bistable has an output of (0). That is, this gate must have a fixed output if either input is (0). Looking back at the truth tables, this leads us to the NAND which has an output of (1) if an output is (0). The loudspeaker will need a driver; we are not looking fkr quality in the sound, and so a simple emitter follower will probably do. In the specification the sound was to be pulsed, which suggests another slow astable. This could be another 555 set to 2 or 3 Hz.

The whole system is shown in Figure 8.4 so that it can be checked for faults and simplifications.

Let us start with the reed switch closed by its magnet and the LDR illuminated. The output from the bistable should be (0) and the alarms off. The output from both the magnetic unit and the light unit will be high or (1). We want the gate to give an output of (0), but an OR will give (1). One solution would be to invert the outputs from the transducer units, but a better way would be to change the gate. A gate is wanted with the truth table in the centre of Figure 8.5. You will see that the gate required is a two-input NAND (or a three-input NAND if the third input is left at (1)).

With the bistable output at (0) the second NAND must have its output at (1) regardless of the state of the astables. No sound will come from the loudspeaker. There is a disadvantage here, remembering that the system is to be battery powered. If the input to the driver is high when the alarm is on standby there will be a large standing current flowing through the loudspeaker, which may damage the loudspeaker and will certainly run down the battery. If an inverter is inserted between the NAND and the driver the

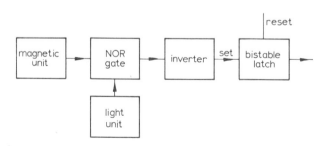

Figure 8.3   Provisional burglar alarm system input

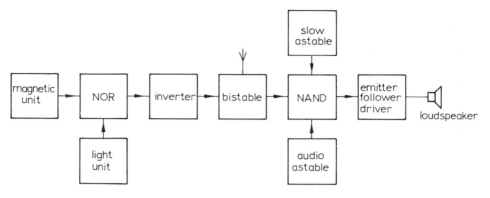

Figure 8.4 Provisional burglar alarm system input and output

NOR					?			NAND			
A	B	C	Q	A	B	Q		A	B	C	Q
0	0	0	1	0	0	1		0	0	0	1
0	0	1	0	0	1	1		0	0	1	1
0	1	0	0	1	0	1		0	1	0	1
0	1	1	0	1	1	0		0	1	1	1
1	0	0	0					1	0	0	1
1	0	1	0					1	0	1	1
1	1	0	0					1	1	0	1
1	1	1	0					1	1	1	0

Figure 8.6 Burglar alarm system with input and standby modifications

loudspeaker driver will be turned off during standby. See Figure 8.6 for the revised system.

The next step is to imagine the input transducers triggered in turn and see that the alarm comes on correctly. When the reed switch opens the output from the magnetic unit will fall to zero. The input to the NAND gate will be connected to zero by the lower resistor in the potential divider. It is rarely wise to drive a logic gate directly from a transducer unit as the high and low voltages are not clearly defined. In other words, a transducer unit does not act as a true switch. A comparator between the magnetic unit and the gate would give a more reliable result. This is even more the case for the light unit, which is unlikely to give outputs which could be clearly (1) or (0). A comparator here would be a great improvement. When the bistable is set to (1) the second NAND will have an output of (0) each time both the fast and slow astables are (1). The output from the inverter is illustrated in Figure 8.7. This will produce the correct pulses of sound in the loudspeaker.

We are now left with the key switch. This will be a single-pole switch that is closed when the key is 'locked' and open when it is 'unlocked'. If the switch was simply connected to $+V_{CC}$ and the bistable reset it would operate as required. When closed it would hold the bistable output at (0) regardless of the state of the input transducers.

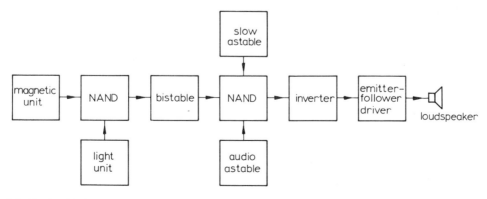

Figure 8.5 Truth table for gate required

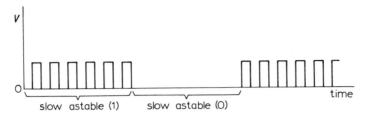

Figure 8.7   System output

When turned to open the alarm would stay off until triggered.

The system is to be battery powered. A good loud noise will need a large low-resistance loudspeaker which will draw a large current. The most suitable battery would be a small 12 V car battery. The supply voltage is therefore fixed at 12 V.

The complete system, shown in Figure 8.8, can now be converted to a circuit. The circuit is shown in Figure 8.9 together with photographs of it assembled out of Electrolern units and built out of discrete components on breadboards. The next stage would be to check the circuit through with a meter stage by stage, but this is impossible in a book and must be left to the reader.

8.7   A sound-operated switch

This second example of the design procedure uses amplifiers and logic ICs.

Specification

The completed device will allow any one of a number of devices to be switched on by a handclap. The device is to have five states, four switching on relays so that mains equipment can be controlled, and the other an off state. The device will step through the states at each handclap. The particular state that the circuit is on at any time is to be indicated by an LED. The device is to be mains powered.

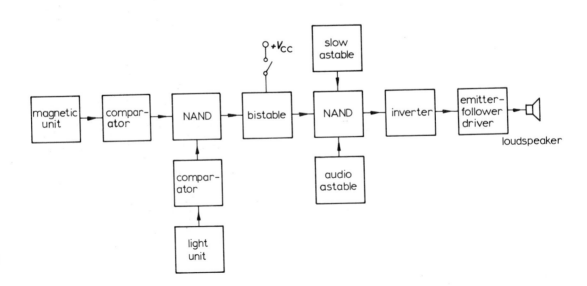

Figure 8.8   Final system for burglar alarm

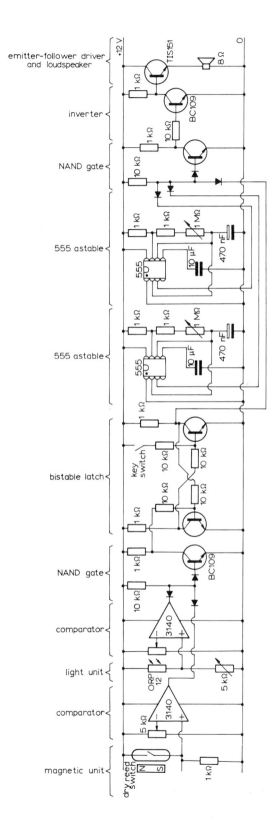

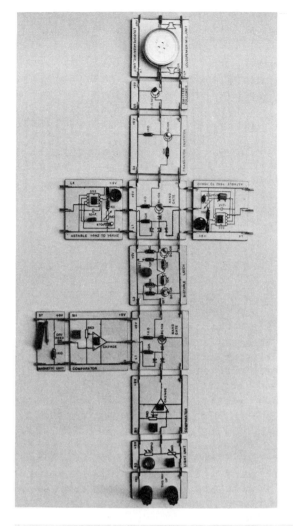

Figure 8.9 Burglar alarm circuit, Electrolern units and breadboard construction

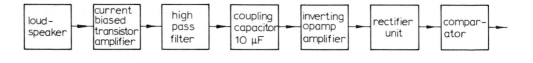

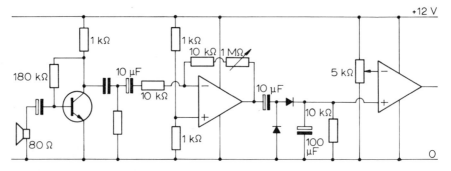

Figure 8.10 Sound-operated switch: input

The input transducer will be a microphone, an inexpensive choice being an 80 Ω loudspeaker used in reverse.

This must be followed by a pre-amplifier. We can expect an output of only a few millivolts, and so the pre-amplifier will need a high gain but an input impedance of only 1 kΩ (10 × 80 Ω = 800 Ω). A cheap and simple solution would be a current-biased inverting transistor amplifier.

Handclaps contain a lot of high frequencies. If the circuit is not to be triggered by other noises in the room, a high-pass filter will need to follow the pre-amplifier.

Next will come the main amplifier, which should be of variable gain. The inverting opamp amplifier will be ideal. The output from the amplifier will be AC with a $\frac{1}{2}V_{CC}$ bias.

This voltage has to be converted to a DC voltage which varies with the amplitude of the output signal. The rectifier unit was designed for this purpose. The rectifier unit will be followed by a switch circuit. The comparator has the advantage that the switching level can be adjusted.

The system so far is shown in Figure 8.10. Each handclap or other sharp noise should make the output give a voltage pulse. You should check that it will.

The second part of the device will consist of a counter, decoding gates and drivers for the LEDs and the four relays. Some logic ICs will be needed, but which ones, and which family? From

Chapter 6 it is clear that for a divide by five counter we shall require three toggle bistables and a gate to decode the fifth state. CMOS is the first choice, which suggests the 4013B dual D-type flip-flop. Two would be required, and one not used. This one must have its reset input connected to V_{DD}.

The counter can have the three required states decoded by NAND gates as in Figure 8.11 using the 4023B triple NAND.

Three drivers will be needed to give the current required by the relays, and the system is complete. Decoding with NANDs gives output of (0), and if the drivers need (1)s a set of inverters will be needed between the NANDs and the drivers.

The logic system is growing, and it would be worth a further search to find a single chip to replace the individual ICs. The 4017B is a decade counter with built-in decimal decoder.

There is obviously more thought and research required before construction can begin. This project has been designed, however, to illustrate the way in which you should proceed and not as something to construct. No details have been given as to how the relays should be connected to the devices to be turned on and off.

If you should undertake a project of this kind and the devices to be controlled are mains driven, *make sure that you receive advice from a qualified person before you proceed, and only connect to the mains while under suspervision.*

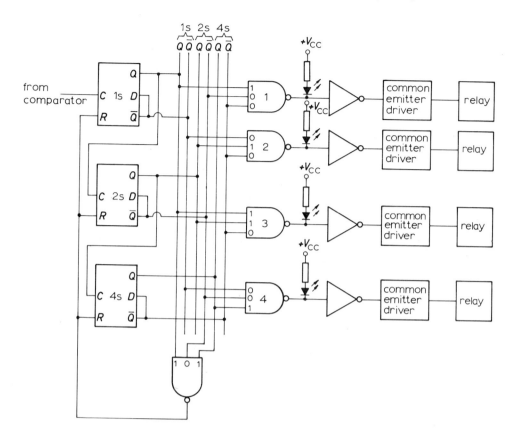

Figure 8.11 Sound-operated switch: output stages

8.8 Circuits into hardware: matrix board

Once the circuit has been designed and checked it must be built permanently. Any circuit consists of a number of connections between component leads. These connections are made by soldering the leads to a piece of conducting material, usually copper. The various constructional methods use different types and arrangements of the conducting material.

The original method was to hammer copper nails into a wooden board, one for each connection, and solder the leads to the nails: hence the term *breadboard*. A modern version of this consists of a laminated paper (SRBP) board pierced with a matrix of holes into which special pins can be pushed. The components are soldered to these pins. The pins either stick out on one side of the board like the nails, or they can be of the double-sided type so that both sides of the board can be used. If the components are spread out

well and their leads left long, this method offers some of the advantages of a breadboard system in that the circuit can quite easily be changed and if unwanted the components can be reused.

Another way of using matrix board is to push the component leads through the holes and just solder them together on the other side with no additional conductor.

In either method there will be places where the component leads will not reach and different connection points will have to be joined by a wire. The wire to use is single-strand tinned copper (tinned means covered with a thin layer of solder). This connecting wire usually goes on the opposite side of the board to the components and is not insulated. If wires have to cross and would therefore short-circuit together, you can use plastic or rubber tubing called sleeving which can be slipped over one of the wires. This is easier than using insulated wire, which is very difficult to strip in short lengths. Never use multistrand wire for making connections on the board. It cannot be bent so that it stays in position like the solid wire, and fine wires tend to stick out at solder joints and make unintended connections.

An advantage in either of the matrix board methods is that the components can be arranged so that they are in the same position as in the circuit diagram, making fault finding easier.

Figure 8.12(a) shows the astable of Figure 8.2 built on to matrix board. The dotted areas on the circuit diagram represent the connections that have to be made. At least eight pins would be required, but more can be used to give a more convenient arrangement and then joined by wire.

It is often a good idea to run two copper wires along parallel to the top and bottom of the board to act as power rails (Figure 8. 12(b)). They can be secured to the board by passing the wire through holes at intervals, the majority of the wire being on the back of the board. Power leads and the leads to components like the potentiometer which is to be mounted off the board will need to be flexible, and so multistrand insulated wire must be used. Where the wire joins the board, first pass it through a hole and back through the next, opening up the holes if necessary. Then strip the end of the wire, twist the strands together, tin it and solder it on. Passing the wire through the holes acts as a cable clamp so that the solder joint is not subjected to strain (Figure 8.12(b)).

Using 0.1 inch matrix board it is possible to mount IC holders. The holder pins are pushed through the board and bent outward to be soldered to pins pushed into the next row of holes. If a large number of ICs are to be used, another constructional method should be considered.

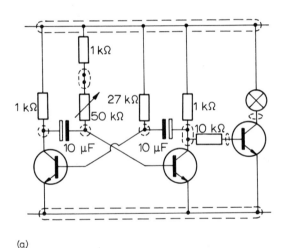

(a)

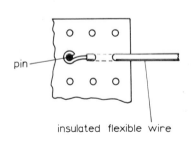

(b)

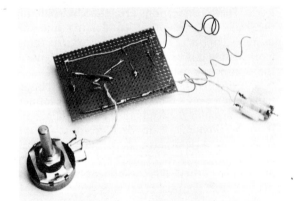

Figure 8.12 Astable of Figure 8.2 built onto a matrix (*a*) Circuit diagram and front of board, (*b*) reverse of board and connection method for flexible leads.

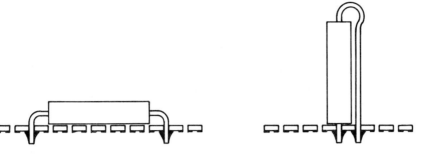

Figure 8.13 Mounting of resistors on stripboard

8.9 Stripboard

Stripboard, or Veroboard as it is often called, consists of an 0.1 inch matrix board with copper strips on one side. It is available with larger spacings and with strips on both sides, but the form described is the most common and the most useful.

The copper strips take the place of the metal pins and electrically connect the components and mechanically support them as well. At least one strip will be required per junction, and a junction of three wires will need a strip three holes long.

Using this information it is possible to calculate the size of board required for a circuit, and you will find that the most complex circuit can theoretically be fitted on to a board a few centimetres square. The catch is that there has to be room for the components on the other side, and the most common mistake when using stripboard is to try to make the circuit on too small a space. Never use adjacent strips but leave an unused strip in between – two if possible. Two strips near the edge of the board are usually left as power rails. Strips often have to be cut so that they can be used for more than one junction. A special tool is available to do this, or you can use a drill. In either case make sure that the strip is completely broken. A magnifying glass is an essential tool when using stripboard.

Components are usually laid flat on the board, but resistors can be mounted end-on as shown in Figure 8.13. This saves space, but if you are wise you will avoid it as the resistors can lever the copper strip off the board, which is a disaster. For the same reason mount the components touching the board so that they are not accidentally pushed down.

Figure 8.14 shows the astable built on stripboard. Wire links on the board should be of solid wire, and leads off the board made of stranded wire secured through holes.

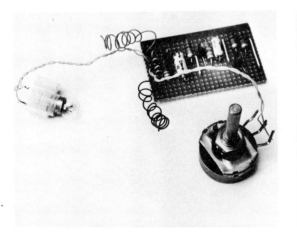

Figure 8.14 The front and back of the astable built on stripboard

8.10   Printed circuit board

Printed circuit board is an SRBP or fibreglass board coated on one side with a thin layer of copper. The areas of the copper, called lands, required to connect the components are marked out by painting over the copper, and the remaining copper is etched away by a solution of ferric chloride. Holes are then drilled in the board for the component leads and the components mounted as in stripboard. The advantage is that the copper strips can be any shape and few additional wires are required. Industry can produce printed circuit boards mechanically in large numbers very cheaply, so they have become the standard construction method.

For the individual who only needs a single board it is a slow and expensive process, and mistakes are difficult to put right. If you do attempt your own board, do not copy the professional and design a pattern where most of the copper is removed and the components are connected by narrow copper 'wires'. Your 'wires' will probably etch away, and the ferric chloride used will be expensive. Instead aim to remove as little copper as possible by designing large lands. For simple circuits it is often possible to design an arrangement of lands in which they are all squares or rectangles, and the 'etching' can be done by a length of hacksaw blade or a sharp knife.

Figure 8.15 shows some circuits which are constructed on printed circuit board.

8.11   Specialized boards

These are somewhere between stripboard and a printed circuit. The arrangement of copper on the back of the board is more complex and has some particular application in mind. A useful type has pads ready to accept DIL integrated circuits or their holders surrounded by a pair of power rails. See Figure 8.16.

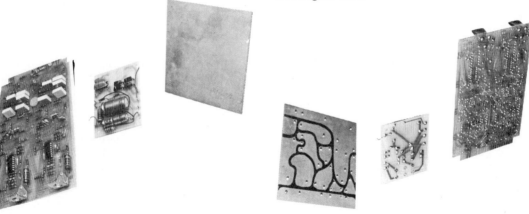

Figure 8.15   The front and back of circuits constructed on printed circuit board

Figure 8.16   Circuit boards

8.12 Soldering

Solder is an alloy of lead and tin, and when molten it can be used to stick metals together so that a conductive path is maintained. To do this the metal surfaces have to be clean. It is hoped that the solderer will do his bit by cleaning the surfaces to be soldered with fine glasspaper or steel wool, but even this is not clean enough, and for electrical work a special flux-cored solder is used. The flux vaporizes on heating and chemically cleans the surfaces to be soldered. The object then is to hold the metals to be joined in contact with a hot soldering iron and a length of cored solder, until the flux has cleaned the joint and molten solder has flowed over the two pieces of metal. The iron and solder can then be removed and the solder will solidify. The problem is that to do the above requires at least two pairs of hands, and we have only one. The method described is shown in pictures in Figure 8.17.

The lack of the extra pair of hands drives learners into using bad techniques which give poor results. The worst is to put the solder on the iron as one operation and then transfer it to the joint as another. The flux burns off before the solder reaches the joint and a poor joint is made. The iron should be held in one hand and the solder in the other. The board and the component must be held by an assistant or by some mechanical means. Use can be made of vices, crocodile clips and bulldog clips. Remove the solder before the iron, and do not allow the component to move while the solder is solidifying.

If it is essential that you hold the work in one hand, a good joint can be made without additional solder or flux by tinning both surfaces to be joined. Tinning a surface consists of cleaning it and then sandwiching a small piece of cored

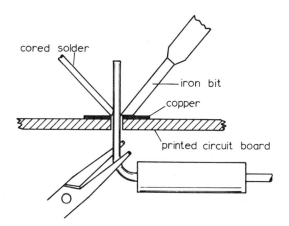

Figure 8.17 Soldering

solder between the surface and the iron so that molten solder flows evenly over both. If both surfaces are tinned and then held together and a hot iron applied to them, the solder on the surfaces will flow to join them.

Attempts to solder dirty surfaces or without flux or at too low a temperature result in *dry joints*. These may not be as shiny as good joints, may have a rounded appearance (see Figure 8.18) and may allow movement of the component. Dry joints sometimes do not electrically connect the two surfaces; more often they form a high-resistance path which deteriorates with time and can cause trouble days, weeks or even years later.

8.13 The soldering iron

A soldering iron consists of a heat-insulated handle, an electrically insulated heating element and a bit. Heat is conducted to the bit which is usually removable. A 15 to 25 W iron with a

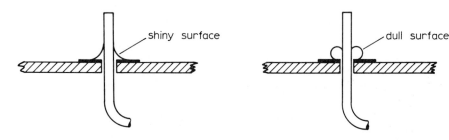

Figure 8.18 Solder joints. The joint on the right is a dry joint

2 mm bit is suitable for electronics. Most soldering irons are mains driven and are therefore a double safety hazard. You can burn or electrocute yourself. The most important safety precaution is to have and use a proper soldering iron stand. This gives you somewhere to put the hot iron between joints and also act as a heat sink and stops the temperature of the iron rising too high. Soldering irons have a nasty habit of committing suicide by burning through their own mains lead and joining themselves to the mains in the process. The use of the stand should avoid this, and as an additional precaution choose an iron with heat-resistant cable. The best choice of all is a low-voltage (usually 24 V) iron with thermostatic temperature control and its own mains transformer with integral stand.

There are two kinds of bit available. Copper bits are cheaper but have to be tinned at intervals and reshaped with a file as the flux corrodes them away. Iron-clad bits are more expensive but last much longer. They must not be filed, but should be cleaned when hot by wiping on a damp sponge. Figure 8.19 shows a low-voltage iron and some soldering and desoldering tools.

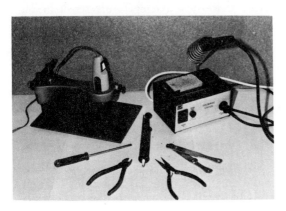

Figure 8.19 Low-voltage soldering and desoldering tools

8.14   Hand tools

The minimum tools required are long-nosed pliers, wire strippers, diagonal cutters and a drill.

The pliers are used for bending component leads and for holding leads when soldering to act as a heat shunt (see Figure 8.17).

Wire strippers remove the insulation from connecting wire.

Diagonal cutters can clip off component leads close to the board.

The drill is needed to drill holes in the circuit board. A hand drill will do, but a low-voltage printed circuit drill is best.

Sooner or later you will make a dry joint and will want to try again, or you will solder a component in the wrong place. In either case you will want to desolder a joint. Here the *solder sucker* is very useful. It is like a small bicycle pump that sucks rather than blows. You melt the solder with the iron and use the tool to suck up the molten solder.

8.15   Testing faulty circuits

The knowledge of electronics required to test a faulty circuit is much greater than that required to build it, with the result that many projects are never finished.

Prevention is much better than cure, and you should follow the procedures described in this chapter to try to avoid faults as much as you can. Nevertheless you will be faced one day with a circuit board that refuses to work as intended.

Let us divide the problem circuits into three classes.

(1) Bought items of electronic equipment which did work but have become faulty. Friends will provide plenty of these.

(2) Circuits built from books and magazine articles which failed to work when completed.

(3) Circuits which you have designed yourself.

Class 1 circuits will be on printed circuit board and no circuit diagram will be available. Fault finding in this situation requires advanced detective work. Use a voltmeter to check that power is reaching the circuit board. If not look for a blown fuse or a lead unsoldered. Check for components that look black or run hot. Turn the board over and look for cracks in the copper strips. These cracks occur when the board is bent and often need a magnifying glass to detect. If the circuit is an amplifier you can inject a signal from a signal generator and see if it comes out of the loudspeaker. If it does the fault must be before this point. Do not adjust potentiometers or the cores of inductors. They were set correctly and if you adjust them you will add more faults to the ones already there.

Class 2 circuits are often like class 1 with the additional hazard that there may be errors in the construction. This time you have a circuit diagram and your first step is to check through, comparing your circuit with the diagram, to make sure that they are the same. Quite often the practical layout in magazine articles is not the same as the circuit diagram.

Class 3 circuits should present a much easier problem. If you have built your system stage by stage, testing as you go, the fault will be in one basic circuit.

Most faults occur when you translate the circuit diagram to a stripboard or other layout. It is very easy to push a lead through one row too far or to fail to break a strip so that it joins different parts of your circuit together. Check the circuit with a magnifying glass. You will be amazed how crude the solder joints look, and you may well find short-circuits and partly broken tracks that you had not suspected.

The next step is to check the transistors, if used. A simple first test is to connect a voltmeter between ground and the collector and use a wire to short-circuit the base to ground. If the transistor is good it must turn off and the voltage across it will rise. This test will not work if the transistor is already turned off and its collector voltage is high. In this case use a $1 \text{ k}\Omega$ resistor to join the base to V_{CC}. The transistor will turn on and its collector voltage will fall. If from these tests you think the transistor is faulty, remove it from the circuit and test it with an ohmmeter. Remember that an NPN transistor can be considered as two diodes facing away from the base region. Use the ohmmeter to ensure that both diodes conduct in one direction and not in the other.

Many circuits will contain one or more opamps. One input will be the reference. Check with the voltmeter that this is neither V_{CC} nor zero. Measure the voltage between the output and ground. Join a lead from the other input to ground and then to V_{CC}. The output should go high for one and low for the other. With logic ICs change the inputs from high to low and so check the truth tables.

Most amplifier faults are caused by incorrect bias and loading. Check both using a CRO. Set the line so that zero is the bottom line on the screen, and switch the AC/DC switch to DC. This way it is possible to see exactly what is going on, bias as well as signal.

Lastly do not forget to test the test equipment itself. I have spent many frustrating hours with power supplies turned off, meters that did not read correctly and faulty signal generators.

Happy hunting.

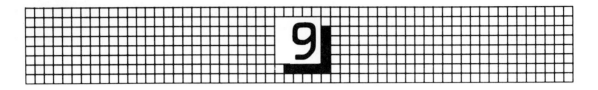

9

Computer systems

9.1 Computer subsystems

The eight previous chapters have been concerned with combining components into basic circuits and circuits into useful systems. The digital computer is such a system. In this chapter we shall adopt the opposite approach – trying to understand how a complex system works by breaking it down into its subsystems.

Any digital computer can be divided into four subsystems: the *central processing unit*, *memory*, *input* and *output* (Figure 9.1).

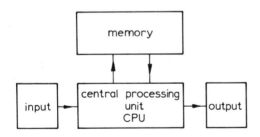

Figure 9.1 Computer subsystems

9.2 The central processing unit (CPU)

This subsystem can be further divided into two sub-subsystems: the *arithmetic logic unit* (ALU) and *control*.

The ALU consists of a block of combinational logic designed to carry out a range of arithmetic and logical operations upon data presented to its inputs. These operations could not take place if the data did not arrive at the inputs at the correct

time, or if the ALU did not receive signals telling it which operation it must perform. These are examples of the tasks carried out by *control*. The heart of control is an astable called the *clock*. The clock drives a counter, and it is outputs from this counter which ensure that operations occur at the correct time.

The CPU contains some memory of its own in the form of storage registers. Many of these registers are general purpose and can be used by the programmer and by control for temporary storage of data. The number and arrangement of these registers varies from one CPU to another, but there are some specialist registers such as the *accumulator*, the *buffer* register and the *program counter* which are to be found in all CPUs (Figure 9.2).

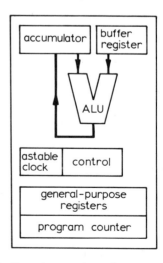

Figure 9.2 Central processing unit

The *microprocessor* is a complete CPU integrated on to a single silicon chip. This integration has allowed it to be fast, small and cheap, and has led to the production of *microcomputers* available to all, and to electronic control of machinery from dish washers to car engines which were formerly controlled mechanically.

9.3 Computer memory

In a computer the data – the words which have to be printed and the instructions which tell the CPU what to do – are all represented by binary numbers and must be stored in the memory. In Section 6.19 it was described how a register made out of bistables could be used to store binary numbers. A computer memory could and often does consist of a large number of bistable registers. These registers have to be arranged in such a way that it is possible to *write* data into or *read* data out of any of them equally easily. To achieve this, each register is fitted with a set of logic gates which only allow data to flow in or out when a particular binary number, the *address* of the register, is applied to its inputs.

Many thousands of such registers together with their logic gates can now be integrated on to a single silicon chip to form a kind of storage called *random-access memory* (RAM). RAM chips are available using storage methods other than bistables, but all have the same characteristics: it is possible to write into them and read from them, but their contents are lost if the power is turned off. They are said to be *volatile*. All computers have a block of RAM in their memory, and it is this area that is used by the programmer to store his programs and the computer to store its data.

There is also a need for another kind of memory that cannot be changed and is not emptied when the power is turned off (*non-volatile*). This *read-only memory* (ROM) is used to store the computer's *instruction set*, the set of binary numbers which enable the computer to carry out its functions. Fixed data, conversion factors and constants used in calculations are also stored in ROM. It is very expensive to make a ROM, and the cost is only justified if a large number are needed. For single ROMs a *programmable* ROM (PROM) is used. Once the binary numbers have been fixed in a PROM chip they are permanent, but in another kind of memory IC the contents can be erased by exposure to

ultraviolet light and the chip reused. This IC is known as an *erasable programmable* ROM (EPROM).

9.4 Input and output

These are the subsystems that allow the computer to communicate with the outside world. It is most efficient to combine them into a unit called *input/output* containing a number of special circuits known as *interfaces*. Input devices connected to the I/O may include *keyboards*, *paper* or *magnetic tape units*, *disc units* and various sensors, joysticks and graphic tablets using the *user* and *analogue* ports. Output devices may be as simple as a row of LEDs, but may be *seven-segment displays*, *visual display units* and *printers*. User and analogue ports normally allow output as well as input. The general name for any device connected to the I/O is *peripheral*, and each peripheral must have an interface to ensure that the signals given and received by the computer and the peripheral are compatible.

Some devices supply or receive data as a whole binary number or *byte* at a time. These devices need a *parallel interface*. Many peripherals can only accept or supply data one bit at a time, and so require a *serial interface*.

9.5 Bus structures

As indicated by the arrows of Figure 9.1, each of the subsystems of a computer is connected to the others. If each possible source and destination of data in the system were connected by a wire, the whole system would disappear under a maze of wires and repair would be impossible. Three kinds of signal can be identified that must be transmitted through the system. These are (1) data, (2) the addresses of the memory locations where the data is located or is to be stored, and (3) control signals which go out from the control section of the CPU to all parts of the system, making sure that the correct operation take place in the correct order.

Each of these signals consists of binary numbers and can be sent along a *highway* or *bus* made up of a number of parallel wires equal to the number of bits in the binary numbers. The designer of a computer decides how many bits he will have in his binary numbers. This standard number of bits is called a *byte*, and all registers in the computer will be made to hold one or

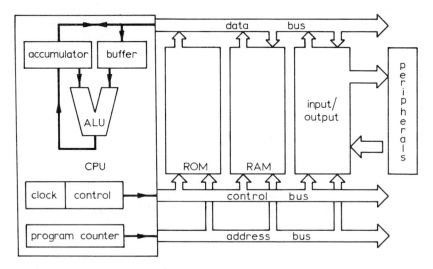

Figure 9.3 Complete computer system

sometimes two bytes. The *data bus* and the *control bus* will be one byte wide, but in the case of the popular, *eight-bit byte* used by many microprocessors the *address bus* is made two bytes or 16 bits wide.

The structure of the complete system is now clear and is illustrated in Figure 9.3. It consists of the CPU, ROM, RAM and input/output joined by three buses. Peripherals are connected to the input/output interfaces, allowing information to flow into and out of the system. The three buses are often taken to a connector so that the system can easily be expanded.

9.6 Tristate logic

The use of a bus structure greatly simplifies the computer system, but it introduces a practical problem. Each bus will have a large number of logic gates connected to it. If one of the logic gates on each wire had its output at zero (0) then the whole bus would be at (0) and it would not be possible to use it. The answer is to use special logic ICs which contain gates with three output states. These states are (1), (0) and unconnected. The unconnected state which leaves the bus able to operate is taken up when an extra control input is set to (1). Figure 9.4 (on this and the next page) explains the action of tristate logic gates by comparing them with their switch equivalents. Figure 9.5 shows how two registers would be connected to a bus through tristate gates.

(a)

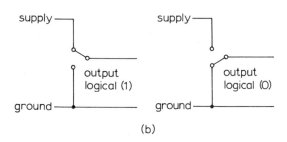

(b)

(c)

Figure 9.4 Action of tristate logic gates (*a*) Normal AND gate (*b*) Possible output states of a normal gate (*c*) Tristate AND gate

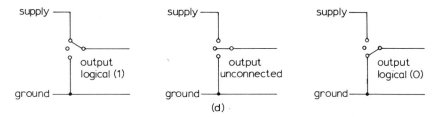

Figure 9.4 (d) Three possible output states of a tristate gate: unconnected state occurs when control is (1)

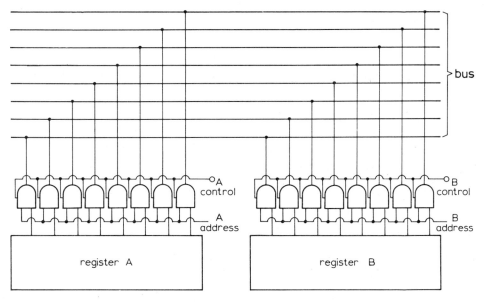

Figure 9.5 Use of tristate logic allows more than one register to feed a single bus

9.7 A microprocessor system in operation

The function of the various subsystems and sub-subsystems that go to make up a microprocessor system (or a mainframe computer) can best be understood by seeing how it carries out a simple task like adding two numbers together.

Before it can start, the programmer must place the two numbers he wishes to be added into the RAM and must note their address.

He then works out a list of instructions for the computer to follow. The tactical plan is called an *algorithm* and is best described by a *flow chart*. A flow chart for the addition of two numbers is shown in Figure 9.6.

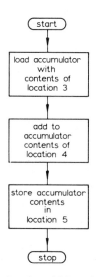

Figure 9.6 Flow chart for addition of two numbers

The algorithm must now be converted to a *program*. Assuming that the two numbers to be added are in locations 3 and 4 (0011 and 0100 are the addresses of these locations) the list of Figure 9.6 instructions) which make up the program can be written in words as:

● Load accumulator with contents of location 3

● Add to accumulator contents of location 4

● Store accumulator contents in location 5

● Stop.

The microprocessor will not be able to understand the words, only binary numbers, and so the program will have to be rewritten in this form. The program is then said to be in *machine code*.

The program uses four instructions: *load accumulator*, *add to accumulator*, *store accumulator* and *stop*. These four instructions will form part of the *instruction set* which the computer has stored in its ROM. Each instruction will have its own binary code. Suppose these codes were

load	0001
add	0010
store	0011
stop	1111

The program in machine code would be

00 010 011
00 100 100
00 110 101
11 110 000

In each line, the left-hand four bits are the instruction and the right-hand four bits are the address of the data. The last line needs no address.

The programmer now decides where in memory he will store his program. He stores it, puts the address of the first line in the program counter (see Figure 9.3), and starts the computer.

The first action of control when a computer is started is always to transfer the contents of the location whose address is in the program counter on to the data bus, where it can be routed into the control part of the CPU. The memory knows that data is to be read from it because a special control line called the *read/write line* is set to (1).

This procedure is called a *fetch* routine. Control looks at the first line of the program and recognizes the instruction *load* and the address 3.

It must now *execute* this instruction. Doing this involves placing the address on the address bus, setting the read/write line to read and copying the contents of location 3 into the accumulator via the data bus. At some time during the execution of the instruction the contents of the program counter is increased by 1. It now contains the address of the second line of the program.

The CPU now carries out a fetch of this byte, decodes and executes it. In this case this will have to be done in stages. First the data in location 4 is routed into the buffer register and then the buffer is added to the accumulator by the ALU. Signals from control make the ALU act as an adder. Once again the program counter is increased by 1, and so the next fetch routine brings the third program line into the CPU to be executed. The address 5 goes on the address bus, the contents of the accumulator go on to the data bus, and the read/write line is set to write. The result is that the contents of the accumulator are written into location 5. The next fetch is decoded by control as stop, and so operation ceases.

9.8 Binary addition

In section 9.7 the ALU had to add two numbers. The two numbers were in binary form, and before we can see how the ALU might have carried out the operation we need to know something about binary addition.

Two single-bit binary numbers are added by a combination logic system known as a *half adder*. Figure 9.7 gives its symbol and truth table. If you cover up the *carry* column the truth table becomes that for the exclusive-OR (Section 6.14). Covering the *sum* column turns the truth table into that for an AND gate. Using this information it is possible to design a half adder in NAND gates.

Consider the addition of the binary equivalents of 45 and 39.

$$
\begin{array}{r}
101\,101 \\
+\ 100\,111 \\
\hline
1\,010\,100 \\
\hline
11\,11
\end{array}
$$

The (1)s below the line are carried from the previous bit. The half adder can only cope with the addition of the LSB. After this the adder needs *three* inputs: *A*, *B* and carry previous (CP).

The truth table will now be eight lines long, and the system to implement it is called a *full adder*. It is possible to make up a full adder out of two half adders plus an OR gate to combine the two carries (see Figure 9.8).

An OR gate can be made out of three NANDs (Figure 6.14), and so it is possible to design a combination logic system for the full adder using NANDs only. This system is shown in Figure 9.9.

In the CPU the numbers to be added would be held in registers. In our example one of the registers would be the buffer register and the other would be a register next to the accumulator known as the *accumulator buffer*. The answer would go into the accumulator. A half adder would be needed for the LSB and a full adder for each of the other bits. This system is shown in Figure 9.10. In addition to the parts shown there would be a number of AND gates which would only route the outputs from the registers through the adders when the correct code was provided by control.

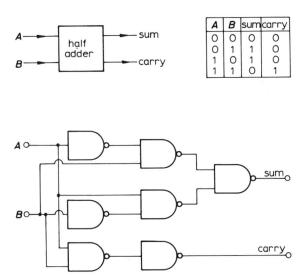

A	B	sum	carry
0	0	0	0
0	1	1	0
1	0	1	0
1	1	0	1

Figure 9.7   Half adder

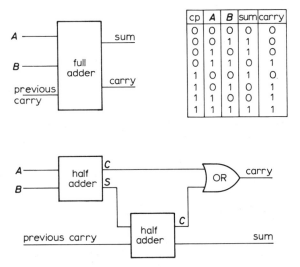

cp	A	B	sum	carry
0	0	0	0	0
0	0	1	1	0
0	1	0	1	0
0	1	1	0	1
1	0	0	1	0
1	0	1	0	1
1	1	0	0	1
1	1	1	1	1

Figure 9.8   Full adder using half adders

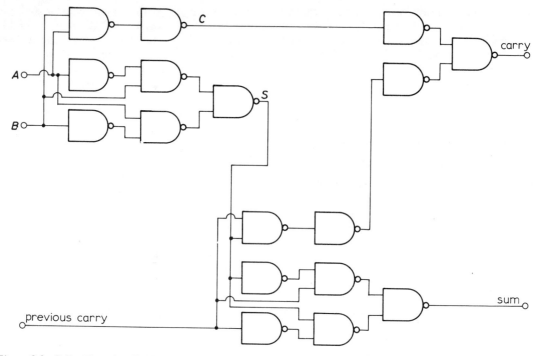

Figure 9.9   Full adder using NANDs only

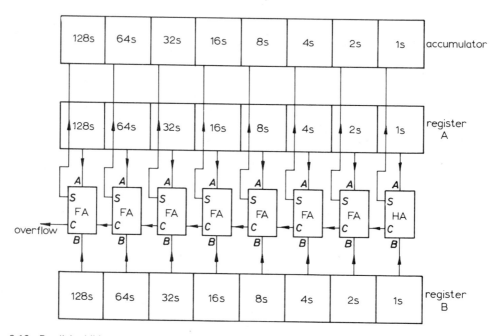

Figure 9.10   Parallel addition

9.9 Binary multiplication

$A \times B$ really means add A to itself B times. Computers are fast enough for multiplication by multiple addition to be practical. There is, however, a quicker way.

Consider the following decimal and binary multiplications:

Decimal:

$$
\begin{array}{r}
784 \quad A \\
\times\ 23 \quad B \\
\hline
15\,680 \\
2\,352 \\
\hline
18\,032 \quad AB
\end{array}
$$

Binary:

$$
\begin{array}{r}
1\,011 \quad A \\
\times\ 101 \quad B \\
\hline
101\,100 \\
+1\,011 \\
\hline
110\,111 \quad AB
\end{array}
$$

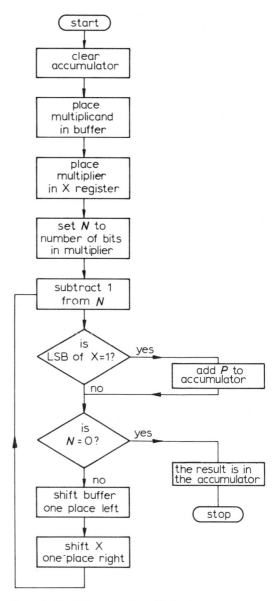

Figure 9.11 Shift-and-add multiplication

The method is exactly the same involving shifting to the left, multiplication and final addition. The binary case is much easier because the multiplication is by either 1 or 0.

The algorithm of a program to carry out multiplication by the *shift-and-add* method is shown as a flow chart in Figure 9.11. To understand the process we will carry it out on an imaginary computer for the binary example above. The computer has an accumulator, a buffer register and another general-purpose register X. Number A is placed in the buffer and B is in X. The computer has an instruction set which includes add to accumulator, shift left one place for the buffer and shift right one place for register X. A number we shall call N which is equal to the number of bits in B can be stored when required, either in another general-purpose register or in RAM. We start with a number in the accumulator left over from the previous calculation. Figure 9.12 gives the contents of the four registers at each stage in the procedure. Multiplication carried out by a program rather than by special circuits is called *software multiplication*.

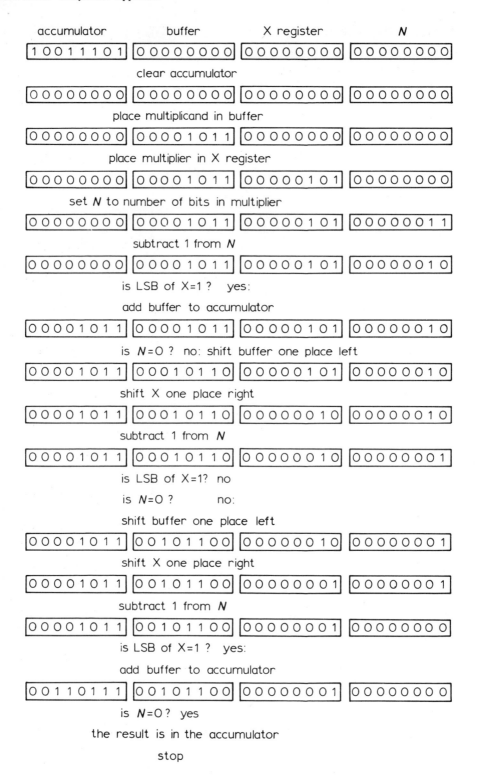

Figure 9.12

9.10 Peripherals

Without some means of entering programs and data and displaying the result, a computer is useless. The most simple input device would be a row of switches and an enter key. Eight switches could represent one byte of data and be entered into the computer's memory when the enter key was pressed. Simple computers using this kind of bit switch usually have other buttons for starting the program and clearing registers. Often the output is displayed on a row of eight LEDs. The programs in this type of computer must be written in machine code and entered line by line. It is very tedious to enter long binary numbers and very difficult to remember them. The combination of these factors makes entering programs with bit switches unreliable. Often the bit switches are replaced by a hexadecimal keyboard. Hexadecimal represents the 16 binary states of a four-bit binary number by the decimal numbers 0 to 9 and the letters A to F:

0000	0	1000	8
0001	1	1001	9
0010	2	1010	A
0011	3	1011	B
0100	4	1100	C
0101	5	1101	D
0110	6	1110	E
0111	7	1111	F

It is then possible to write down or key in an eight-bit binary number as two hexadecimal digits:

4F	is	0100 1111
B2	is	1011 0010

Computers with a hexadecimal pad as input usually have a seven-segment display as output. The display would show the whole range of hexadecimal symbols. To help the programmer, even simple computers have a range of programs stored in ROM that allow any particular register to be displayed on the output, single steps through the program and many similar options. These permanent programs are half-way between wired logic and programs in RAM (software). They are known as *firmware*.

The next great improvement in a computer would be a full *alphanumeric* keyboard like the one on a typewriter. When a key is pressed a binary code number representing the symbol on the key is generated. More than 70 different numbers are required to represent the upper- and lower-case letters, numbers and symbols such as (,/,), +, – etc. The most common code is known as American Standards Code for Information Interchange (ASCII). Part of ROM must be used to store these code numbers. Once the computer has an alphanumeric keyboard it is possible to type in instructions using a limited number of English words instead of binary numbers or their hexadecimal equivalents. ROM now has to store programs that can translate these words into machine code. The words and the rules which govern their use is called a *high-level language* and the program in ROM an *interpreter* or *compiler*.

If it is possible to type in words and numbers, they must be displayed at the output. An early solution was to combine an input keyboard with an output printer in the *teletype*. This looks rather like an electric typewriter, but closer examination shows that it works on a slightly different principle. As an input device the ASCII code is generated by opening or closing a number of electromagnetic switches when a key is pressed. This code is fed into the computer along a single wire bit by bit. When the complete code number has been transferred, the next key can be pressed. This is an example of *serial transfer* of information. When used as an output device the ASCII code is again transferred serially, but this time from computer to teletype. The first two bits are used to select one of four possible heights for a cylinder on which four rows of characters are arranged. The remaining bits specify how far the cylinder is to be rotated. The printing is done by pressing the selected character against a typewriter ribbon which marks the paper (See figure 9.13). The printing mechanism is then moved one step to the right in readiness for printing the next character. There are special ASCII control codes to make the printing mechanism return to the left and advance the paper. The teletype can print at about ten characters per second.

Once a program has been written the operator will not want to type it in each time it is to be used. Some kind of long-term memory is required: a *backing store*. The teletype has its own backing store, consisting of a *paper tape* puncher and reader. When a keyboard key is pressed the puncher records its code as a series of holes across the width of a paper tape. A hole is a (1) and no hole a (0). The program is therefore stored on the tape as a series of rows of holes (Figure 9.14). It is

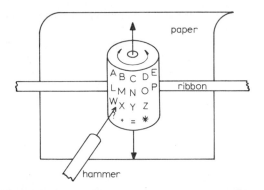

Figure 9.13 Teletype with diagram of printing mechanism

contents of RAM on to paper tape. Using the tape reader the codes stored on the tape can be printed out or fed back serially into RAM. The tape is fed into the reader by sprocket holes formed when the tape was punched, and the presence or absence of holes is detected by metal feelers. Once again the main disadvantage is the slow speed.

In modern computers the most important output device is the *visual display unit* (VDU). The heart of a VDU is a CRT of the type used in television sets. Time base circuits in both the X- and the Y-direction make the spot move across and down the screen in lines, in a manner similar to reading a book. As the spot moves it can be turned either on or off by (1)s and (0)s stored in memory. In this way it is possible to 'print' characters on the screen. Part of ROM must store the codes and control the screen. The great advantage of the VDU is as a programmer's aid, particularly when the programmer is a beginner. The program can be seen as it is typed and errors corrected. Text can often be deleted, moved and changed using a range of editing facilities.

Most computers that use a VDU provide *graphics* which enable lines and shapes to be drawn and combined into pictures.

Compared with the teletype, the VDU is silent rather than noisy and fast rather than slow, owing to it being electronic rather than mechanical. The electronic nature of the VDU should make it more reliable, although teletypes are so well made that they last almost for ever. This unfortunately makes them very much more expensive.

With all its virtues, the VDU does not give a permanent record or provide a backing store. To

also possible to punch a tape at the same time as the teletype is printing out data from the computer. It is therefore possible to dump the

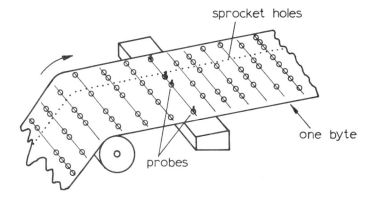

Figure 9.14   Storage on punched tape

overcome the first the computer must be connected to a *printer*. These come in many shapes and sizes, some very like a teletype and some that print very fast with lasers. Some printers accept data bit by bit in *serial* like the teletype and VDU; some accept whole bytes at a time, and are called *parallel printers*.

The cheapest available *backing store* is the ordinary *cassette recorder*. This was designed to record music, not binary codes, and so the bits are recorded on the tape in series as notes of different frequency for (1)s and (0)s. You can hear them if you play the tape. When the tape is played back the cassette interface circuits convert the tones back to binary bits. The cassette recorder is a slow and not very reliable backing store, so where the expense can be justified they are replaced by *floppy disc* systems where the bits are recorded as magnetic 'spots' on a disc made of the same kind of material as cassette tape.

Figure 9.15 shows some of the output devices.

9.11 Uses of computers

Computers are now used in such a wide variety of applications that it is impossible to think of one that is typical. However, the applications can be divided into the following:

- A large mainframe computer, able to perform a full range of operations at very high speed, is shared by a number of users.

- A relatively simple CPU is coupled to a large back-up store to carry out data processing.

- Small mini- or micro-computers are used by one individual at a time in what is known as an *interactive* way.

- Microprocessor/memory combinations are built into machinery to carry out automation and process control.

The first type of application might be in the science faculty of a university, and would carry out all the calculations and data storage of the

Figure 9.15(a)   VDU (visual display unit)

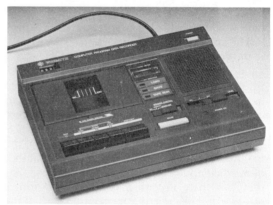

Figure 9.15(c)   Cassette recorder

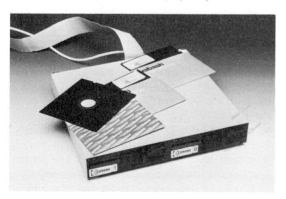

Figure 9.15(b)   Disk drive and disks

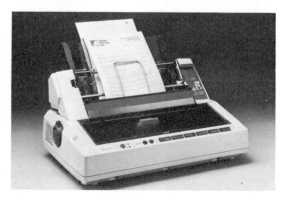

Figure 9.15(d)   Daisy wheel printer

various departments. The computer would have to have a terminal in each department, the computer dividing its time between each. For example, if there were 10 users the computer might spend 10 ms on each terminal in turn, giving each user the impression that he alone was using a machine of one-tenth the actual speed. During slow input/output operations the computer could get on with its other work while waiting for the printer to need the next character. The CPU of a time-shared computer with this use would have to be able to carry out the advanced mathematical operations required as well as the usual data processing.

The second kind of use might be a supermarket with laser readers at its checkouts. The computer would hold records of the stock and the ideal number of each item that should be stored. The computer could then print out orders for items that were running low. Its records would be continually updated by the information from the checkouts. The CPU would not have to carry out any complex arithmetic, but it would need advanced data processing capabilities. Most of the data would be held on a large, fast backing store.

The university science departments mentioned in the first example might well prefer to each have an individual minicomputer with its own VDU, printer and store. It would then be possible for individuals to enter data, wait for the answer, and on the strength of this answer continue with their calculation. This is an example of interactive use.

It is possible to combine the advantages of the first and third applications by linking a number of microcomputers together by a network so that they can share expensive peripherals. Another way is to install a microprocessor into each of the terminals of a time-share computer so that each is a microcomputer in its own right.

Domestic machines like dish washers and washing machines work through one of a number of set routines. In the past they have been 'programmed' by switches operated by a motor-driven shaft, but if they contain a microprocessor the program can be stored in ROM. The customer benefits from the reliability of electronic circuits, the manufacturer benefits from their low cost and from the ease with which he can introduce new models; they need only different trim on the outside, and a new ROM.

A microprocessor and a program in ROM can be made to simulate any logic function, and so it is becoming common to use a microprocessor rather than to wire together logic gates. Many machine tools are engaged with their operator in making the same object over and over again. The machine can be controlled through suitable interfaces from the input/output of a microprocessor system, and again the program is stored in ROM. New work just means a new ROM. Industrial robots go one stage further. They contain operating programs in ROM as before, but also an area of RAM so that they can react to some extent to changing circumstances. They can be fitted with sensors for touch, heat and even vision, and programmed to react according to the outputs of these sensors in a way that approaches the way we react. (See Figure 9.16.)

Figure 9.16   An industrial robot

Any task that can be exactly defined can in theory be carried out by a microprocessor-controlled machine or robot, and these are the very jobs that human beings find most boring. The introduction of microprocessor control therefore removes workers from dull jobs and gives them the more interesting jobs which involve complex decision-making and dealing with people.

Microprocessors also raise efficiency and reduce costs. If costs are reduced, more people will be able to afford the product, more will be sold and so we would hope that the same number of people would be employed making more of the product more efficiently and so earning higher wages. This may not happen. Instead the same amount of the product may be manufactured as before at a greater profit and with a smaller workforce. The people who before had boring jobs then have no jobs at all. No one knows whether the microprocessor revolution will help all people or only some people, but it is certain that it is happening anyway.

Questions

1 What do you understand by the abbreviations ROM, RAM, PROM and EPROM?
You have just written a word processor program in machine code, and you are going to store it in one of the above and plug it into your computer.
Describe the advantages and disadvantages of using each of the four alternatives, and explain why the program would have to be written in machine code.

2 Any computer can be considered as consisting of four main parts. Name these parts, and explain the function of each. Which of these functions can be carried out by a microprocessor?

3 Draw up a flow chart which would enable a robot to make a cup of tea.

4 'A simple computer has an address bus which is 6 bits wide.' Explain the meaning of this statement, in particular making clear the meaning of the terms 'address bus' and '6 bits wide'.
How many bytes of memory would this computer be able to address?

5 The simple computer described in Section 9.7 has an output display consisting of eight LEDs, each showing the state of the bistables which make up the register whose address is 0001.
Draw up a flow chart and convert this to a program in machine code which would make the LEDs display the three times table in binary.
You may use the instructions given plus the following branch instruction:
Branch back . . . steps: The operating code is 0100 and number of steps is given in the following four bits: 01000100 means branch back four steps. You must count the branch instruction as one of the steps.

6 A computer carries out a cycle of operations consisting of fetch-decode-execute over and over again.
Describe these three operations.

7 While a computer was running a program, a fault caused the program counter to increase its contents by 5 suddenly. How would this affect the running of the program?

8 The data bus of a microprocessor system can be used to enter data into the memory or extract data from the memory.
Explain how the memory knows whether the data is to flow in or out.

9 Convert the decimal numbers 27 and 34 to their binary equivalents. Add the two binary numbers and convert the answer to hexadecimal.

10 Explain the function of the following parts of a microprocessor: clock, program counter, ALU, accumulator.

11 What is the difference between hardware, software and firmware in a computer?

12 Give three examples of computer peripherals. Describe the functions that the interfaces connecting these peripherals to the computer will have to perform.

13 Buses can be unidirectional (transfer binary numbers in one direction only) or bidirectional (transfer binary numbers in both directions). State, with your reasons, which of the three buses in a microprocessor system is most likely to be bidirectional.

14 Write down the truth table for a half adder. Design a combinational logic system which will produce this truth table using
   (a) Any logic gates
   (b) NAND gates only
   (c) NOR gates only.

15 Why is it not possible to add two binary numbers of more than one bit using half adders only?

16 It is possible to carry out the multiplication of two binary numbers in a computer by multiple addition rather than shift and add. Draw up a flow chart for multiplication by multiple addition and, by comparing it with the flow chart for shift and add, discuss the merits of the two systems.

Communication systems

10.1 What is communication?

Communication has been described as the transfer of ideas from one brain to another. The brains need not belong only to human beings, as a great deal of communication goes on between animals. However, this chapter is concerned mainly with electronic communication systems, which are the preserve of man.

The ideas to be communicated may be facts, opinions or questions, but they are all classified under the heading of *information*. Much information is today stored in computer memories and needs to be transferred from one computer to another. We therefore need to extend our definition of communication to include communication between machines.

10.2 What is a communication system?

The best way to answer this question is to examine in detail a communication system which is very familiar to us all – speech. An essential for any communication is a *medium* joining the person who wishes to send the information, the *source*, and the person who is to receive it, the *receptor*. In the case of speech the propagation medium is the air, and in particular its pressure. The source uses his vocal chords and cavities in his head and mouth to make changes in the pressure of the air so that it carries a coded form of the information he wishes to convey. This process is called the *modulation* of the medium. The speech waves are then *transmitted* through the source's mouth. The waves spread out from the source, and some will enter the receptor's ears where the pressure waves are converted back to nerve impulses to the receptor's brain. The ears act as a *receiver*. The receptor's brain is able to convert the signals back to ideas again, and the communication is complete. The recovery of the information from the modulated medium is called *demodulation*.

The whole system is represented by a block diagram in Figure 10.1, and you will notice in this diagram that there is no mention of the type of

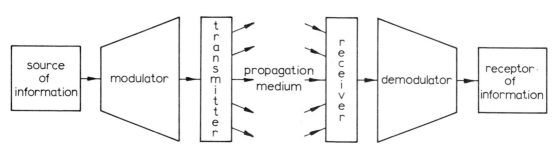

Figure 10.1 Communication system

communication it represents. The diagram can be used to describe any of the systems in this chapter, and as each one is discussed you should refer back to Figure 10.1 and identify each block in the new system.

10.3   Early systems of communication

Speech is very convenient at short range, but it is a poor system for long distances. The energy in a sound wave is soon lost as the wave travels through the air. We say that the sound is rapidly *attenuated* by distance.

Man wanted to send information rapidly over long distances and looked for a medium that would allow him to do so. The most suitable available medium was light. News of important events could be sent from one end of a country to the other by lighting a series of signal fires placed on hill tops. This system was limited by the very simple way the medium was modulated. The fire was either lit or it was not – an early binary code. The meaning of the fire had to be prearranged.

Later the fires were replaced by signal lamps which could flash short or long beams of light. The use of the *Morse code* (Figure 10.2) allowed more complex modulation of the carrier so that real communication could take place. An alternative to the signal lamp is a person holding two flags. The position of the flags is made to represent letters or numbers and so communication can take place (Figure 10.3). An interesting feature of both these systems is that although the carrier of the information is light, which travels at very high speed, the complete system is very slow. The slow speed stems from the *serial* nature of both systems (sending one character at a time) and from the time required to code and decode each character.

If a microphone is connected to a CRO and speech patterns are examined, they are seen to consist of a continuous variation. Signal of this type are known as *analogue* to distinguish them from signals consisting of a series of off and on states which are called *digital*. It would be very convenient if the analogue signals of speech could be directly modulated on to a medium or *carrier* so that they could be communicated over long distance as they are over short distances in normal speech. Two systems were used before the discovery of electricity: the *speaking tube*, where the source and receptor were joined by a tube, and the *string telephone*, where they are joined by a stretched string. These systems are shown in Figure 10.4, and in each case normal sound waves are used but their attenuation is reduced. In the speaking tube the sound energy is concentrated inside the tube, and in the string telephone the wave in the air is converted to a wave in the string.

Morse Code

		M — —	T —
A ·—	G — —·	N —·	U ··—
B —···	H ····	O — — —	V ···—
C —·—·	I ··	P ·— —·	W ·— —
D —··	J ·— — —	Q — —·—	X —··—
E ·	K —·—	R ·—·	Y —·— —
F ··—·	L ·—··	S ···	Z — —··

Figure 10.2   Morse code

Semaphore alphabet

Figure 10.3 Semaphore chart

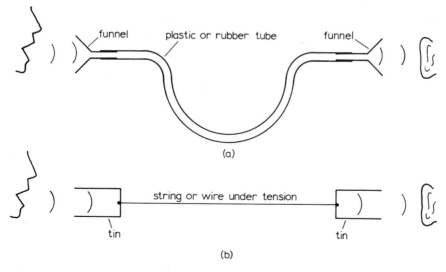

Figure 10.4 Systems for transmitting sound

10.4   The electric telegraph

All the systems described in the previous section except the speaking tube suffer from the same disadvantage: the source and receptor have to be able to see each other for the system to work. (Try taking the string of a string telephone round a corner.)

With the discovery of electricity the transmitter and receiver could be joined by insulated wires. The electric telegraph was an electrical version of the signal lamp. A key switch was used to tap out short *dots* or long *dashes* so that the medium was the current and the modulations on it were digital in nature, using the Morse code. Various systems were used at the receiver to detect the dots and dashes. The one illustrated in Figure 10.5 consists of a buzzer (an electric bell without the bell), so that the operator could hear the signals and have his hands free to write.

10.5   The telephone system

The telephone system was invented by Alexander Graham Bell in 1877. Figure 10.6 shows a simple telephone system of just two *handsets* and batteries. Each handset contains a carbon microphone and an earpiece of the type described in Section 7.17. Whichever microphone is spoken into, an alternating voltage will be induced in the secondary of its transformer. This voltage will be the analogue of the sound wave reaching the microphone, and it will drive a similar current through both earpieces. The great advantage of this system is that it is two way; either person can be the source or the receptor.

The simple system shown would not be a practical one. The batteries are replaced by power

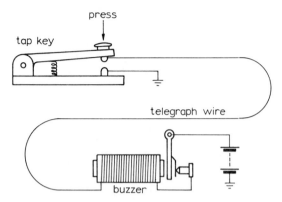

Figure 10.5   Electric telegraph

lines, and a rest for the handset is designed so that it switches off the power when the telephone is not in use.

10.6   The Strowger exchange

In a telephone system, any two telephones must be able to be connected. The connections are carried out at an *exchange*. In early systems a handle was turned on the receiver to gain the operator's attention. The caller simply told the operator the number of the telephone required, and the operator made the connection by linking sockets with plugs and leads.

It was an easy matter for an operator to listen in on private conversations. Almon Strowger was an undertaker in Kansas, and his rival's wife was an operator at the local exchange. Strowger believed that the wife was diverting his customers to her husband, and he decided to invent a way of connecting calls automatically. In 1889 he suc-

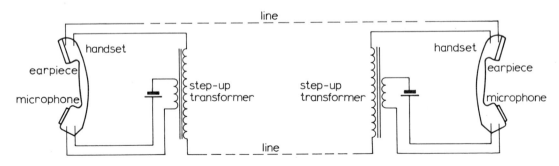

Figure 10.6   Simple telephone system

Figure 10.7 Alexander Graham Bell, the inventor of the telephone system

ceeded. An automatic system needs a method by which the caller can tell the exchange which number he requires in a form that the automatic machinery can understand. The form chosen was a series of voltage pulses produced by a *dial* (Section 10.7). The Strowger system was based on a special kind of relay. Each pulse from the caller pulled in the relay and moved a wiper one step round a circular arc of contacts. Each digit in the telephone number moved a different relay, so a complete number connected up a unique pathway through the contacts, joining the telephones. Figure 10.8(a) shows a picture of a relay of the type described, called a *uniselector*. More complex two-motion selectors are also used, where the wiper arm can move vertically as well and make contact with any of a stack of ten arcs of contacts. (Figure 10.8(b)).

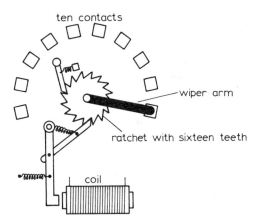

Figure 10.8(a) Uniselector relay

10.7 The telephone dial

Suppose the dial in Figure 10.9(a) is turned so that the number 7 comes up against the finger stop. If the dial is then released it will return to its original position at a preset speed. As it does so, cams close a switch seven times and seven voltage pulses are sent along the telephone wire. During dialling the exchange receives the correct number of pulses for the number dialled in sequence.

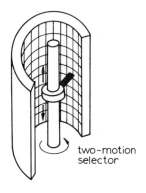

Figure 10.8(b) Two-motion selector

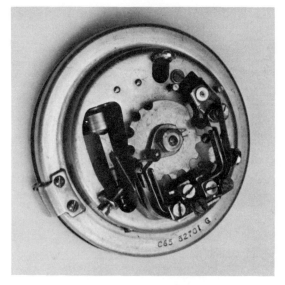

Figure 10.9(a)   The front and back of a telephone dial. Pulses are sent by the switch shown at the bottom of the dial on the right

Some modern telephones have push buttons instead of a dial (Figure 10.9(b)). Electronic circuits inside the telephone send out the correct number of pulses when a button is pushed, so that the result is the same as if a dial had been used.

Figure 10.9(b)   Modern push-button telephone

The exchange attracts the attention of the subscriber dialled by sending an alternating current down the line. If the receiver is on its rest a switch is operated which routes this current to the bell circuit (Figure 10.9(c)) and the bell rings. When the receiver is lifted, the bell is disconnected.

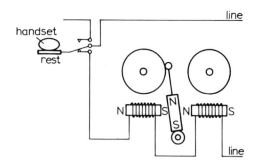

Figure 10.9(c)   Telephone bell circuit

10.8   Crossbar exchange

The Strowger exchange was reliable but slow. The faster crossbar system (invented by Homer Roberts in 1916) is a grid system based on horizontal and vertical rows. At each point where the rows cross there is a relay which, if operated, will join them. Each digit in the dialled number activates a particular relay, and so a unique path is established through the grid.

10.9 The present telephone system

Electronic circuits have been invented which can perform the tasks formerly carried out by relays. This has led to the introduction of *all-electronic exchanges* which work on the *common-control* principle. This means that once a particular call is set up the control equipment is available for the next. This and the electronic circuits give a faster and even more reliable exchange.

One of the limitations of a telephone system is the number of lines. If there are more people in London who want to call someone in Leeds than there are lines between London and Leeds, then obviously some will have to wait. The problem can be cured by either putting up more lines, which is very expensive, or sending more than one conversation down each line. The technique used in the second solution is called *multiplexing*. In *frequency-division multiplexing* each conversation signal is modulated on to an AC signal of different frequency, and then all the signals are sent down the wire. At the receiving end, filters are used to separate the different frequency carriers and the different signals are routed to their destinations. (For more detail on modulation of a carrier, see the sections on radio in this chapter.)

Time-division multiplexing has already been met in Chapter 9 as a method of allowing several terminals to use the same computer. Each of the conversation signals is sampled rapidly in turn, and the samples are sent down the wire in succession. The receiver has to be synchronized with the transmitter if the individual signals are to be sorted out at the other end.

In the present analogue telephone system, FDM is the more suitable method.

If the telephone system is to stretch round the world, not all routes will be suitable for telephone wires. Along some, use is made of short-wave radio waves called microwaves to carry the signal. Copper wires are everywhere slowly being replaced by *optical fibres* (Figure 10.10), which can carry more signals with less attenuation. Optical fibres use internal reflection to contain the light signal. Whatever the medium there will always be some attenuation, and the signal will gradually decrease in amplitude until it is too small to be detected. To prevent this there are amplifiers called *repeaters* at intervals along the route. These repeaters restore the signal to its original amplitude, but they also amplify the random voltage *noise* which is present in any electrical system. At the receiving end this noise sounds like a hiss or crackle, and therefore although the loudness of the received sound may be adequate the quality of the sound may deteriorate until it is difficult to understand what is being said.

Modern telephone systems are used for other purposes besides the transmission of speech. Pictures can be sent by *facsimile transmission* and computers linked by the telephone line. Prestel is British Telecom's viewdata service, whereby a large central computer is connected through the telephone line and a special interface to a domestic TV set and a keyboard. Information from the computer can be displayed on the TV screen, and action can be taken on the information given by sending messages back down the line. In this way it is possible to order goods or book holidays without leaving home.

10.10 System X

System X is the name of a new British Telecom telephone system based on digital electronic exchanges which will gradually replace the existing system in this country. All the signals entering the exchange – voice, computer data, facsimile,

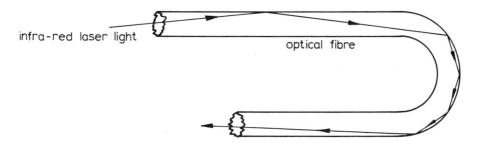

Figure 10.10 Optical fibre

telex or video – are handled by the same computer-type circuits under the guidance of computer programs. This is called an *integrated digital network*. Its introduction will mean that the exchange of information of all types over the telecommunications network will be faster and greatly simplified for the user.

Speech signals will no longer be transmitted in analogue form but by using a method called *pulse-code modulation*. The voltage of the analogue signal is *sampled* at frequent regular intervals and the values converted to binary numbers. (See the analogue-to-digital converter, Section 2.5.) The binary numbers are sent serially along the telephone wire, and at the receiver a digital-to-analogue converter turns them back to voltages. The reconstructed waveform will only be an acceptable reproduction of the original if the sample rate is very high. A sample rate of 8 kHz is used, with the voltages recorded as 8-bit binary numbers. Each voltage is therefore rounded up or down to one of 256 *quantum* voltage levels. This is found to be satisfactory for sound between 300 Hz and 3400 Hz.

A sample rate of 8 kHz means that one eight-bit number must be transmitted each 1/8000 of a second. Modern digital ICs can do this in much less, and then must wait until it is time to send the next sample. Meanwhile the telephone wire is not being used, and other signals can be sent. This is an example of time-division multiplexing.

Pulse-code modulation (PCM) may appear to be a very complicated way of transmitting a signal, but it has one great advantage over an analogue method. You will remember from Section 10.9 that long-distance communication and the quality of shorter-distance signals is limited by noise. Amplifiers cannot tell the noise from the signal, and both are amplified. Digital signals are either (1) or (0). As long as it is possible to tell which is which, a circuit like a Schmitt trigger can be used to cut out the noise and restore the signal to its original quality. Circuits

of this type are called *regenerators*, and they are used at intervals along a PCM line. When these advances in telecommunication are fully available and combined with advances in computing and data storage, it seems likely that few people will have to travel to work as the information will come to them in their homes.

10.11   The electromagnetic spectrum

Figure 10.11 shows the whole family of electromagnetic radiations. They all have some properties in common – their high speed and their ability to pass through a vacuum – but other properties depend on their wavelength and frequency. These two quantities are linked by the equation

$$velocity = frequency \times wavelength$$

Visible light has already been mentioned as a medium for communication, and their speed and freedom from attenuation make the other members of the family potentially useful for the same purpose. The radiations with a frequency greater than visible light can be dangerous to health, so it is to those of longer wavelength and lower frequency that we turn.

To use a section of the electromagnetic spectrum as a carrier of information we must be able to transmit, modulate and receive it.

10.12   Radio transmission and reception

A radio transmitter contains an oscillator which oscillates at the frequency of the wave to be transmitted. If the output of the oscillator is connected to a wire or rod called an *aerial*, an electromagnetic wave will be radiated into space. A common type of aerial, called the *half-wave dipole*, is illustrated in Figure 10.12. A similar

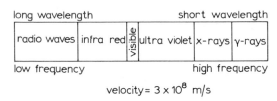

velocity = 3×10^8 m/s

Figure 10.11   Electromagnetic spectrum

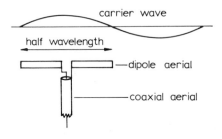

Figure 10.12   Half-wave dipole

aerial at the receiver would convert part of the energy from the wave into an alternating voltage. The dipole needs to be no longer than half the wavelength of the electromagnetic wave, because at this length it experiences all possible variations in the wave.

A half-wave dipole would not be a practical aerial for low-frequency waves as their wavelength would be too long, but dipoles are greatly used to receive VHF radio transmissions and for television reception. If a dipole is rotated in a vertical plane, the strength of the signal varies from maximum to zero. The wave is said to be *polarized*. If you compare the old VHF television aerials still on the roofs of houses with the smaller UHF type, you will see that the VHB signals were polarized vertically but the UHF are polarized horizontally.

10.13 The range of radio transmissions

Electromagnetic waves consist of perpendicular magnetic and electric fields (Figure 10.13) and do not interact with the materials through which they pass. They suffer very little attenuation, and can travel over very large distances provided that no solid body is in between. Unfortunately, because the earth is a sphere it lies between points on its surface which are a long distance apart, and would appear to make long-distance radio communication impossible. Two factors make this untrue.

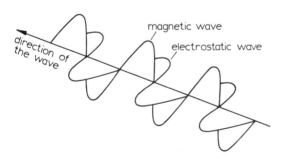

Figure 10.13 Electromagnetic wave

At the lower frequencies an electromagnetic wave suffers a *ground effect*: that is, the wave tends to follow the curve of the earth and so reach further than expected.

Ionized layers in the upper atmosphere, the Heaviside and Appleton layers, reflect radio waves above 20 MHz. Short-wave radio signals directed upward, the *sky wave*, are alternately reflected by the ionized layers and the earth and *skip* round the world, making worldwide communication possible (Figure 10.14).

10.14 Choice of waveband

Starting at the low-frequency end, the radio part of the electromagnetic spectrum is divided up into a number of *wavebands*, each with its own properties and uses.

Long wave (*low frequency*) These waves have frequencies between 30 kHz and 500 kHz, giving wavelengths of thousands of meters. A half-wave dipole would not be a very practical aerial. These long waves are very good at spreading round corners by *diffraction*, and so a single high-power transmitter can serve a whole country. BBC Radio 4 at 200 kHz and 1500 m is in the LF waveband.

Medium wave (*medium frequency*) 500 kHz to 1.5 MHz. These waves are also diffracted, but more transmitters are required to give full coverage. This is the most popular waveband, and so it is divided up into sections 5 kHz wide, with each being given to a different station. BBC Radio 1, 2 and 3 transmit on the medium band.

Short wave (*high frequency*) This waveband has less diffraction, and mountains and hills form 'shadows' of poor reception. This waveband is not used for general broadcasting but for communication between ships etc.

Very high frequency At this frequency diffraction is much less, and the range of a transmitter is reduced. In some ways this is an advantage because there is less interference between different stations. This waveband has been chosen by the BBC for its high-quality radio transmissions, and was formerly used for low-quality TV.

Ultra high frequency Suffers from shadows behind hills and buildings, so frequent repeater transmitters and good aerials are required. Used for colour TV transmissions.

10.15 Modulation

As in any system of communication, the information to be transmitted must be modulated on to

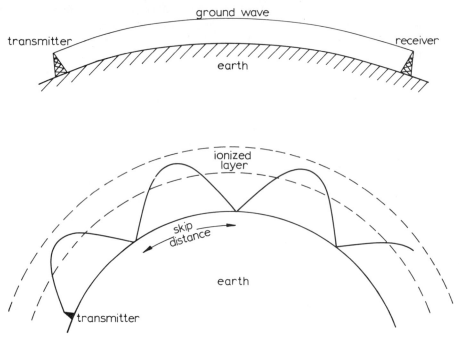

Figure 10.14   Ionized layers in the upper atmosphere

the carrier. This is done before the wave reaches the transmission aerial. Figure 10.15 shows a block diagram of a transmitter, and graphs of the wave to be transmitted, the carrier wave and the modulated wave. Inside the modulator the wave to be transmitted and the carrier are multiplied together. The type of modulation illustrated is called *amplitude modulation*, and is used on the first three wavebands.

A carrier wave is a pure sine wave, but when modulated its shape has changed. According to Fourier the new shape could be obtained by adding a number of other sine waves of different frequency to the carrier. If the carrier frequency is F and the modulation frequency is f, these extra frequencies lie between $F-f$ and $F+f$. The difference between these two frequencies is the space in the waveband that the modulated wave will take up, and is called its *bandwidth*. The extra frequencies are known as *sidebands*.

Imagine that a speech signal with 3 kHz as its highest frequency was to be amplitude modulated on to a carrier of 200 kHz. The highest and lowest sidebands would be 197 kHz and 203 kHz, giving a bandwidth of 6 kHz (Figure 10.16).

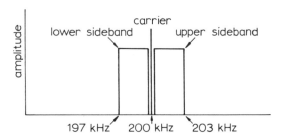

Figure 10.16   3 kHz signal on 200 kHz carrier

10.16   Simple radio receivers.

We have seen that the first stage in a receiver is an aerial. Down the aerial will come all the radio stations which are transmitted, and some circuit will be required that can *select* the one we want. The receiver must then *demodulate* the signal so that the modulation wave is recovered, and then this wave must be converted to sound by an output transducer.

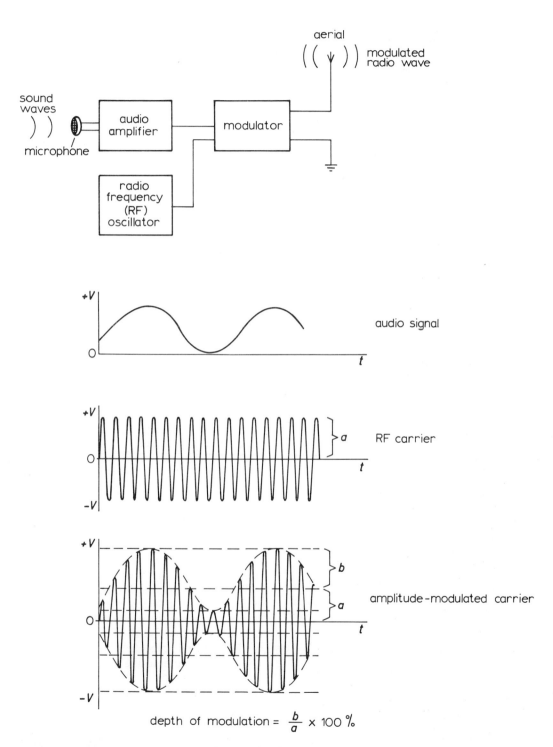

depth of modulation = $\frac{b}{a} \times 100\%$

Figure 10.15 Communication through amplitude modulation

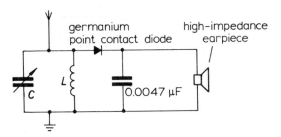

Figure 10.17(a)   Simple diode receiver

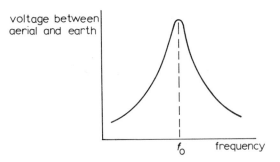

Figure 10.17(b)   Selection of correct station

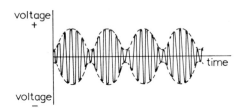

Figure 10.17(c)   Modulated voltage

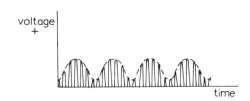

Figure 10.17(d)   Rectification

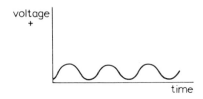

Figure 10.17(e)   Original signal

Look at the simple diode receiver (crystal set) of Figure 10.17(a). The correct station is selected by a *tuned circuit* (Figure 10.17(b)) consisting of an inductor and a variable capacitor. The circuit has a low impedance for all frequencies except one, the carrier frequency, given by

$$f_0 = \frac{1}{2\pi \sqrt{(LC)}}$$

with the result that all frequencies except this one are short-circuit to earth. A modulated voltage is developed across the tuned circuit (Figure 10.17 (c)).

In a practical circuit the inductor could be 60 to 80 turns of insulated wire on a ferrite rod and the capacitor a trimmer of 250 pF capacitance. The

aerial could be as long a wire as possible, and a good earth is essential.

Once the correct signal has been selected it drives a current through the point contact germanium diode and is rectified (Figure 10.17(d)). The capacitor filters out the radio frequency part, and the original audio signal passes through the earphones (Figure 10.17(e)). All the energy in the sound must come from the wave, so it will be very quiet. One of the amplifiers of Chapter 7 could be used to increase the power into the earpiece.

We have two choices. Either we can amplify the signal directly it leaves the tuned circuit and before it reaches the diode demodulator, or we can amplify the signal after it has been demodulated and smoothed. In the first case the voltage will be alternating at radio frequency, and an amplifier which is able to operate at these frequencies will be required. Such amplifiers are known as *radio frequency* (RF) amplifiers. The basic circuits which use opamps cannot be used as RF amplifiers because opamps are limited to frequencies below about 100 kHz. Our RF stage would have to be one of the transistor amplifiers. A BC109 will operate well at radio frequencies.

Figure 10.18 shows how a current-biased amplifier could be coupled to the tuned circuit.

Once the signal has been rectified and smoothed, it is alternating at *audio frequency* (AF). Any of the basic circuit amplifiers, including those using opamps, could be used to increase the amplitude of the audio signal. The class B output stage could be added so that the radio could drive a loudspeaker. A radio of this kind is called a *tuned radio frequency* (TRF) radio.

is shown in Figure 10.20 and described below. It should be looked upon as an experimental circuit, and as such can give some useful insight into the working of a radio.

The aerial consists of about 60 turns on a 6 inch ferrite rod in parallel with a 250 pF tuning capacitor. The radio signal is taken from the tuned circuit by between three and five turns of wire wound on top of the aerial coil. This signal goes to the base of the first transistor, which is

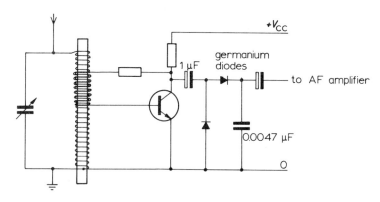

Figure 10.18   RF amplifier coupled to tuned circuit

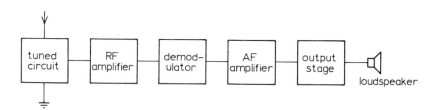

Figure 10.19   Basic radio

The whole system is illustrated in Figure 10.19. Do not expect too much from a radio of this type. Several stages of RF amplification is usually required to give a large enough signal, and amplifiers with large gains operating at high frequencies are subject to spontaneous oscillations which produce a variety of 'pops' and 'whistles' out of the loudspeaker rather than Radio 1.

If we want to build a TRF radio that will work, we must use cunning methods that obtain very large gains out of a few transistors. Such a circuit

connected in common-emitter mode, and receives voltage amplification. The output is directly connected to the base of the second transistor. At radio frequencies the choke in the emitter of this transistor has very high impedance and so the stage can be considered as emitter follower, giving high input impedance to avoid loading the first stage while giving a low-impedance output. The choke consists of 100 turns of wire on 1 inch of ferrite rod. After leaving the emitter follower, the RF signal is rectified by the detector diode and smoothed by the 0.0047 μF capacitor. The

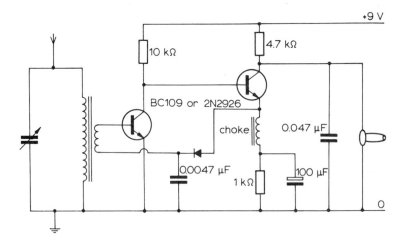

Figure 10.20   Tuned radio frequency radio set

detected audio frequency signal is fed back to the base of the first transistor, which now acts as a common-emitter AF amplifier. The choke has low impedance to AF and so the second stage becomes common emitter and the further amplified AF signal is available at the collector. The 0.047 μF capacitor filters out any remaining RF. The output can be fed to a crystal earphone or into an output stage.

If the choke is constructed with long leads and held near to the aerial, one of two effects will be observed. The signal strength will decrease, or it will increase perhaps so much that the receiver breaks into oscillation. To change from one to the other, invert the choke. In one case we have negative feedback from choke into aerial, and in the other we have positive feedback, in this case called *inductive regeneration*. It is also possible to obtain *capacitive regeneration*. Join lengths of insulated wire to the top of the aerial and to the collector of the first transistor and then twist them together. The simple capacitor so made will feed signal back into the aerial, either in or out of phase depending on the sense in which the pickup turns were wound. Because of its use of regeneration, this would be called a TRF *reflex* set.

The main defect of the simple TRF set with a single tuned circuit is poor *selectivity*: that is, it finds it difficult to separate one radio station from the stations on either side. Selectivity can be improved by having several tuned circuits and RF amplifiers (tuned RF amplifiers) in series. Each

has to have its own tuning capacitor, and all have to change frequency together. This is achieved by controlling all the capacitors by the same shaft, i.e. ganged capacitors. It has proved very difficult to design a set of tuned RF amplifiers which are always tuned to the same frequency throughout their range, and this difficulty has led to the invention of the *superhet* described in the next section.

As in most branches of electronics, a radio IC has been developed. This is the ZN414, and it is a TRF radio tuner with *automatic gain control* or AGC. AGC is a system which turns up the gain of the RF amplifier when the signal is weak and turns it down when it is strong, giving a constant output. The RF part of a radio based on this chip is shown in Figure 10.21. Add your own AF stages.

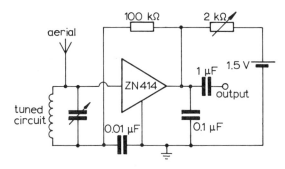

Figure 10.21   RF section of a radio based on the ZN414. The 2 k Ω potentiometer controls the level of automatic gain control

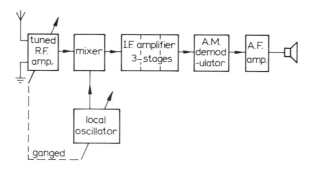

Figure 10.22 Superheterodyne receiver

10.17 The superheterodyne receiver (superhet)

Most radios today are superhets, using the system shown in Figure 10.22. The first part of this type of receiver is an aerial and tuned circuit with its output amplified by a radio frequency amplifier. The signal is then multiplied by the output of an internal oscillator, the *local oscillator*. The result is the production of two frequencies, a sum and a difference. (See amplitude modulation, Section 10.15.)

The difference signal, called the *intermediate frequency*, is amplified by several stages of IF amplifier and then passed on to a *demodulator* or *detector*. The audio signal has now been obtained, so it can be amplified and passed into the loudspeaker. Both the tuned circuit and the local oscillator contain a variable capacitor, and these are mounted on the same shaft (ganged) so that both frequencies vary together and the difference, the IF, remains the same.

The advantage of the superhet is that the IF amplifiers only have to amplify one frequency, and other frequencies can be rejected. This is a great advantage in crowded wavebands, as it makes it possible to separate the wanted signal from the stations on either side.

10.18 The radio and telephone systems compared

Radio is at its best when broadcasting information to a large audience. The telephone is most suitable for person-to-person communication, where the lack of privacy in radio is a disadvantage. Modern telephone systems can move slightly into the province of radio with *conference calls*. These allow a number of telephones to be connected at the same time so that the users can have a conference without having to meet.

Sometimes radio must be used where a telephone would be more suitable. In some parts of the world there are no telephone wires, and person-to-person communication has to be carried out by radio. This is also the case when one or both of the communicators is moving. Each channel will require its own frequency band so that different calls do not interfere with each other.

10.19 The transmission of pictures

Mention has already been made of facsimile transmission the sending of still pictures along a telephone wire or a radio link. The picture is scanned at the transmitting end by a light-sensitive device such as an LDR. The scan starts at the top left-hand corner, moves along horizontally, and then moves rapidly back to a point directly below the starting point and begins its next horizontal line. In this way the whole picture is scanned line by line in the same manner as you would read the page of a book. This is called a *raster scan* (Figure 10.23). The light-sensitive device forms part of a circuit that gives an output voltage proportional to the brightness of the picture. The analogue voltage signal produced is sent to the receiver just as though it was a speech signal. At the receiver a pen is mechanically moved over a sheet of paper so that it carries out a raster scan exactly synchronized with the transmitter. The pen marks the paper to a density controlled by the analogue signal so that the original picture is reproduced.

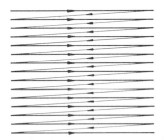

Figure 10.23   Raster scan

10.20   The transmission of moving pictures: television

A television camera contains a lens which projects an image of the scene before it on to a small screen. This screen is scanned in a raster scan by a beam of electrons which, as in facsimile transmis-

sion, produces an analogue signal proportional to brightness. Where in facsimile work the scan may take minutes, the raster for TV is completed in 1/50 of a second. The scan continuously repeats itself and the signal is modulated on to a radio wave as carrier and transmitted. Instead of a pen, the TV set has a CRT with its spot moving in a raster scan synchronized with the camera. The carrier is demodulated and the recovered analogue signal is used to control the brightness of the spot. A picture is built up on the screen every 1/50 of a second, and the eye and brain combine individual pictures into one that moves.

Let us look at the system in a little more detail. Figure 10.25 shows the production of a video signal by a TV camera. Compare the camera tube with the CRT used in a CRO (Section 2.14). In the camera tube the electron beam is deflected by magnetic fields produced by coils. Time base circuits drive currents through these coils of the form shown in the graphs. As the field current increases, the beam moves from the top to the bottom of the screen, and in the flyback period it moves rapidly back to the top ready to start again. The field coils by themselves would produce a vertical line of electrons on the screen but,

Figure 10.24   A television camera in use

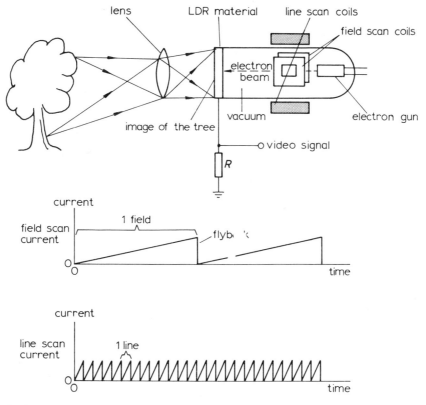

Figure 10.25 Production of a video signal by a television camera

when the line scan current adds horizontal movement to the beam, the result is a raster scan. The graphs would give only thirteen lines in a field, while our television pictures consist of 625 lines. The CRT in the TV receiver is similar in construction to the camera tube except for the screen, which is much larger and covered with a *phosphor* rather than LDR material.

Time base circuits in the set generate sawtooth waves of exactly the same form as those in the camera. It is very important that the timebase circuits in the receiver and those in the camera are exactly in step if the picture is to be accurately reproduced. This is achieved by adding *synchronization* pulses to the video signal from the camera so that the time base circuits in the receiver know when to start their field and line scans. The resultant *composite video signal* is then modulated on to a carrier and transmitted. The information content in a video signal is much greater than in an audio signal and requires a much greater bandwidth. In order that the

available waveband can accommodate as many TV channels as possible, the bandwidth of each channel must be kept as small as possible. This is done in two ways:

(1) The bandwidth could be halved if one raster scan took 1/25s instead of 1/50 s, but the lower frequency of repetition would produce unacceptable flicker. The solution is to use *interlace*. Every other line of a complete TV *frame* is transmitted in 1/50 s, followed by the rest of the lines in a further 1/50 s. The complete frame takes 1/25 s but it consists of two 1/50 s fields. The eye thinks the picture is repeating at the faster rate and so does not notice flicker, but the bandwidth is halved.

(2) The modulated carrier consists of two side-bands as shown in Figure 10.26(a). Each sideband, after interlace, is now 5.5 MHz wide, giving a total bandwidth of 11 MHz. It has been found that the higher-frequency

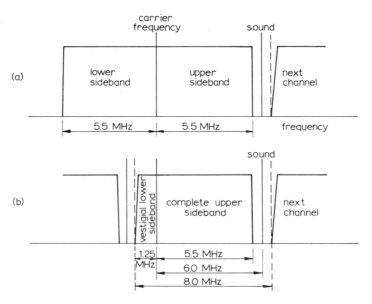

Figure 10.26   Lower sideband suppression

part of the lower sideband can be suppressed with acceptable loss of detail in the resulting picture. Figure 10.26(b) shows a complete 625 line channel. The sound is modulated on to a separate carrier spaced 6 MHz above the vision carrier. The sidebands are too small to see on this scale, but are wide enough to give sound of hi-fi quality.

Even though the bandwidth required for a TV channel has been reduced by every available means, it is still very large by radio standards. The whole of the medium waveband would only take one-fifth of a channel. The only answer is to go to higher frequencies for the carrier, and the 625 line system uses the ultra-high-frequency waveband which lies between 470 MHz and 854 MHz. The penalties we pay for the use of this high-frequency waveband are closely spaced transmitters to avoid 'shadows', and more difficulties in the design of the electronic circuits.

10.21   Colour television

Any coloured light can be produced by the addition of the three primary coloured lights *red*, *green* and *blue* in the correct proportions. In a colour camera the light, after passing through the lens, is split up by a special prism into three

identical beams which focus on to the front of three camera tubes (Figure 10.27). In front of each tube is a filter, one red, one green and one blue. Three video signals are therefore produced, each containing the information for one of the primary colours.

Suppose that each of these video signals were modulated on to a separate carrier and could be received by a television receiver. Imagine that this receiver had three electron guns and the brightness of each was controlled by a different 'coloured' video signal. Phosphors are available which will emit red, green or blue light so that if the screen could be covered with dots of the three kinds of phosphor and it somehow arranged that the electron beam for a particular colour only hit its own phosphor, a colour picture would be produced. Such a TV tube is available as the *colour mask tube* (Figure 10.28). The screen consists of dots of red, green and blue phosphor as described above, but between the electron guns and the screen is a metal mask with rows of holes drilled in it. As the three electron beams scan the screen their electrons pass through the holes and activate the appropriate phosphor dot. Even though there are about 500 000 holes in a 26 in tube shadow mask, only about 15% of the electrons in the beams reach the screen and the rest go to waste.

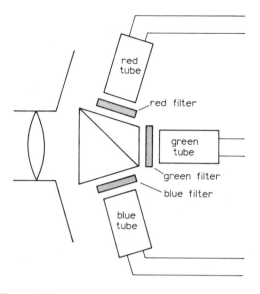

Figure 10.27   Colour camera action

Although the colour mask tube exists, the imaginary system described above cannot be used for two reasons:

(1) Transmitting three video signals would require three times the available bandwidth.

(2) Some people still have *monochrome* (black and white) sets and their sets must still work.

The three coloured video signals are added together to form a *luminance* signal, which contains all the brightness information, can be transmitted just like the old monochrome signal, and will give good pictures on monochrome sets. The colour or *chrominance* signals are combined and modulated on to another carrier and transmitted in such a way that no greater bandwidth is required. The receiver recovers the three chrominance signals from their carrier and applies them to the three electron guns, when the colour picture is produced as already described.

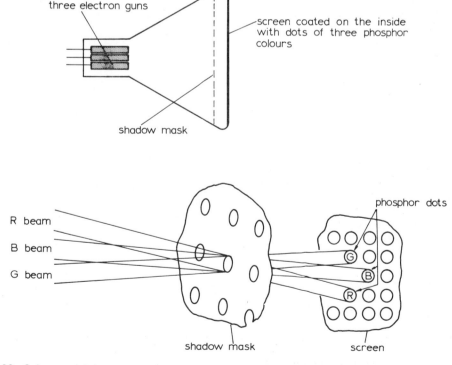

Figure 10.28   Colour mask tube

10.22 Teletext

Not all the 625 lines of a TV picture appear on the screen. Four of these lines in each frame are reserved for teletext information. The information on these lines can be received and decoded by special teletext receivers. These sets, as well as acting like a normal TV, can behave like a visual display unit and display 'pages' of still text and pictures like computer graphics.

A teletext page consists of 24 rows, each 40 characters wide. One line can hold the information for only one row; therefore it will take six frames before a complete page has been transmitted. Each frame takes 1/25 s, giving a total time of 6/25 s for the complete page. The pages are transmitted one after another up to 100, and then the cycle begins again. If you want a particular page you will have to wait until this page comes round, and this might take $(100 \times 6)/25 = 24$ s. Each channel can have a different 100 pages. Those on BBC are called Ceefax, and those on ITV Oracle. They are used to supply constantly updated information on news, sport, weather etc.

The teletext TV set stores the page you require in a block of RAM so that you can see it after its transmission has ceased. It is likely that sets of the future will contain enough RAM to store the whole number of pages available, even when the set is switched off, so that the whole of the teletext information is instantly available.

10.23 Satellite communication

A satellite (Figure 10.29) with an orbit 35 786 km above the equator is said to be in a *geosynchronous* orbit. In this orbit the satellite exactly matches the speed of rotation of the earth and always remains over the same point on the surface. If the satellite is equipped with a radio transmitter and aerial (usually called its *antenna*) it can 'illuminate' an area of the earth, called its *footprint*, with radio waves. Within this footprint earth stations can communicate with each other directly via the satellite. A particular satellite may have several antenna, and so several footprints and techniques exist which enable stations in different footprints to communicate.

Large earth stations using dish antennas of up to 30 m in diameter are used for telephony and TV distribution (Figure 10.30). Medium-sized stations use antennas of 3 to 5 m in diameter and are used for data transfer, facsimile transmis-

sions, telex, and by cable TV distribution companies. Look out for these antennas on office blocks and factories.

Small antennas of about 80 cm diameter can be used for the domestic reception of TV signals broadcast directly from a satellite. These will become increasingly common in the future.

Figure 10.29 Satellite MARECS

10.24 Television in the future

The main use for television has so far been for the provision of mass entertainment, but there are other possibilities. Perhaps each telephone will have its TV screen and we will be able to see as well as hear our callers. Many people use their TV set as a VDU for their home computer and video games. Facsimile pictures can be displayed on a TV screen instead of drawn by a pen, and (as already described) the BBC and ITV both send a series of still pictures called teletext along with the moving pictures for those whose sets are equipped to decode it. In the future it is very likely that one or more microprocessors plus ROM and RAM will be built into the domestic TV set so that when linked to the telephone system it can be the home's information and entertainment centre.

Figure 10.30 Dish antennae at the British Telecom earth station at Malden, Herefordshire

Figure 10.31 Many home computers use a television set as a VDU

Questions

1 Explain the meaning of the terms 'source', 'medium' and 'receptor' in a communication system. Identify these quantities in the smoke signal system of communications used by the American Indians.

2 What do you understand by the expression 'to modulate a medium'?
What is the medium in a string telephone, and how is it modulated?
How does the receiver demodulate the signal?

3 What do we mean by 'noise' when considering an electronic communication system? Why is the signal-to-noise ratio important?
   Explain why it is possible to understand Morse code signals when the signal-to-noise ratio is very low and speech would be unintelligible?

4 'When one is talking on the telephone, one's own voice can be heard coming out of the earpiece.'
   Is this statement true or false? Justify your answer.

5 Describe, with a diagram, the action of a telephone dial. What part does the governor play in its action?
   Explain how dialling the number enables an automatic exchange to connect you to the correct telephone.

6 Describe the working of a telephone bell. Why can it only ring when the telephone is on its rest?

7 'All telephone signals are attenuated as they pass along the wire.' Explain the word 'attenuated'.
   In the present analogue system the attenuation is overcome by repeaters at intervals along the line. Describe the function of the repeaters. Can you suggest another name for them?
   In what way does the quality of the signal deteriorate in spite of the action of the repeaters?

8 What is pulse-code modulation? If the sample rate is 8 kHz, what is the time delay before the next sample has to be transmitted? If an analogue-to-digital conversion takes 2 ns, how many signals can be sent along the same wire?

9 What are the characteristics of electromagnetic waves that make them suitable for the medium in a communication system?

10 The old 405-line TV system was received by vertical dipole aerials over a metre high, but the present 625-line system uses horizontal dipoles that are only a fraction of a metre in length. What does this tell us about the radio waves used to transmit the two systems?

11 Radio waves cannot penetrate the earth, and yet it is possible to receive radio signals from the other side of the world. Explain?

12 'All waves suffer diffraction – a tendency to spread into the shadow – when they are obstructed by an object, but the diffraction is very small unless the object is equal to or smaller than the wavelength of the wave.'
   Use this statement to explain the relative advantages of the different parts of the radio spectrum for use as the medium in a communication system.

13 The low-frequency waveband extends from 30 kHz to 500 kHz and the medium-frequency waveband extends from 500 kHz to 1.5 MHz. If a radio channel has a bandwidth of 10 kHz, how many channels can be fitted into each of the two wavebands?

What will be the highest frequency in the sound that is transmitted by these radio channels?

14 Sketch the waveform of a sine-wave carrier, amplitude modulated by another sinusoidal wave of lower frequency. The carrier has a frequency of 15 kHz, the modulation wave has a frequency of 1 kHz and the depth of modulation is 60%.

15 A 2 MHz carrier is amplitude modulated by a sine wave of 12 kHz frequency. What bandwidth will be required, and what will be the lowest and highest frequencies transmitted?

16 Draw the circuit of a simple diode receiver and explain how it carries out the functions of selection and demodulation.

What are the advantages and disadvantages of this simple receiver?

17 What is the feature of a superhet receiver that makes it superior to that of a tuned radio frequency set? How is this superiority achieved?

18 A radio channel is transmitted in the very-high-frequency waveband on a carrier of frequency 95 MHz. What would be the length of a dipole aerial designed to receive this channel?

19 Draw a block diagram of a superhet radio receiver. Describe how the intermediate frequency is produced, and explain why its frequency remains constant when the radio is tuned to different stations.

20 What is AGC when referring to a radio circuit? Why is AGC essential for a car radio?

21 Both facsimile transmission and television use the raster scan principle but, while television needs a bandwidth of 8 MHz, it is possible to send facsimile pictures along the telephone wires. Describe what is meant by a raster scan, and explain the great difference in bandwidth requirements.

22 What is it that sets the lower limit on the repetition rate of the fields in television transmission?

23 Describe how the electron beam in a camera tube or a television receiver tube is made to carry out a raster scan.

Why is it important that the scans in the camera and the receiver are synchronized, and how is this synchronization achieved?

24 Describe the action of shadow mask tube. How are the three 'colour' signals obtained?

25 It would be possible for all three 'coloured' video signals to be modulated on to different carriers, demodulated by the receiver and used to control the three guns in a shadow mask tube. Why was this system rejected in favour of what appears to be a more complicated system?

26 The bandwidth required by a television channel was reduced as much as possible. Describe two techniques used to achieve this reduction.

Numerical answers to questions

Chapter 1

1

Current	Potential difference	Resistance
		4 Ω
	14 V	
225mA		
	40 V	
		2 M Ω
91nA		
	4.5 V	
170μA		

2 (a) 0.8 A.   (b) 240 C.   (c) 960 J.

3 (a) 80 k Ω, 0.125mA.   (b) 19.4 k Ω, 0.303mA.

4 (1) $10\,000\,\Omega = 10\,k\,\Omega \pm 10\%$, 10K.
(2) $560\,\Omega = 0.56\,k\,\Omega \pm 5\%$, 560R.
(3) $820\,000\,\Omega = 820\,k\,\Omega \pm 20\%$ 820K.
(4) $47\,000\,\Omega = 47\,k\,\Omega \pm 5\%$, 47K.
(5) $39\,\Omega = 0.039\,k\,\Omega \pm 10\%$, 39R.

5 20 mA,   22 V

6 58 mA,   87 V.

7 1000 C. Charge will be shared equally between the capacitors, i.e. 500 C   each.   10 V.

8 Time constant   = 0.47 s.   (a) 0.47 s.
(b) 0.16 s.

9 20.

Chapter 2

1 (b) 66.7 Ω/V.

2 Resistor value = 1114 Ω. Meter reading = 6 mA. Internal resistance = 600 Ω. Battery voltage = 6 V.

3

	(a)	(b)	(c)
Peak-to-peak	4 V	1.1 V	25 V
Peak	2 V	0.55 V	12.5 V
RMS	1.414 V	0.39 V	—
Period	20 ms	750 μs	120 μs
Frequency	50 Hz	1333 Hz	8333 Hz

4 10 k Ω.   For 20 k Ω resistor—2.4 V.   For 10 k Ω resistor—1.2 V.   Digital voltmeter—4 V and 2 V.

5 0.1 A.   0.15 A.

Chapter 3

4 $500\,\Omega$

5

Base/collector		Base/emitter		Collector/emitter	
+ to B	+ to C	+ to B	+ to E	+ to C	+ to E
1 high	low	high	low	high	high
2 low	high	low	high	high	high
3 low	low	high	low	high	low

Transistor 1 is PNP, transistor 2 is NPN, transistor 3 is PNP but with the base/collector diode short circuit

6 (a) 1.3 V.   (b) 0.05 mA.   (c) 3 mA.   (d) 0 V.   **8** 55 mA.   0.28 mA.
h_{FE} of new transistor = 200.

9 $h_{FE} = 100$. $200\,\Omega$

Chapter 4

1 (a) 0.78 A, 7.8 V, 6 W, 0.94 W.   **4.** 6 V.

   (b) 3 A, 4.5 V, 13.5 W, 13.5 W.   **5** (a) 6 V.   (b) 7.5 V.   (c) 4.54 V.

   (c) 4.5 A, 2.25 V, 10.125 W, 30.375 W.   **6** (a) 3 V.   (b) 5.45 V.   (c) 5.9 V.

2 1.5 V, 0.5 Ω.   **11** Current in $2\,k\Omega$ and $4\,k\Omega$ resistors = 2 mA.
Current in $1\,k\Omega$ and R resistors R = $3\,k\Omega$

3 9.23 V, 10.9 V.   = 3 mA.

Chapter 7

1 Sine wave: peak-to-peak = 2 V, peak = 1 V,
RMS = 0.7 V.

Square wave: peak-to-peak = 1 V,
peak = 0.5 V, RMS = 0.5 V.

3

Gain	Frequency (kHz)
20	90.9
80	0.1
24	33.3
60	0.124

4 Total Gain = 1200.

Chapter 9

4 64 bytes.

9 $27_{(10)} = 11011_{(2)}$.

$34_{(10)} = 100010_{(2)}$.

Hex number $= 3D$.

Chapter 10

8 0.000125 s.   62500 signals.

13 Low frequency band—47 channels. Medium frequency band—100 channels. Maximum frequency $= 5\,kHz$.

15 Bandwidth required $= 24\,kHz$. Lowest frequency transmitted $= 1976\,kHz$. Highest frequency transmitted $= 2024\,kHz$.

18 1.58 m.

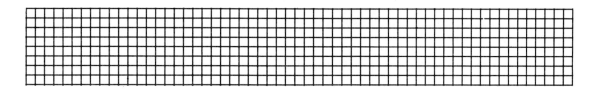

Index